WELCOME

Baking is a wonderful way to get creative in the kitchen. Not only that, the fruits of your labour are delicious treats for your family, friends and colleagues – everyone's a winner! What you'll find here is a special collection of great advice, fun features and over 60 failsafe recipes to try, all selected from best-selling baking books.

Short on time? Then turn to the muffins chapter and all you have to do is decide whether you are in the mood for sweet or savoury, then whip them up in next to no time. Looking for something to occupy the kids in the holidays? Turn to the Cupcake Decorate feature for some wonderful ideas to get the frosting and sprinkles flowing (and be sure to get the kids to clean up the kitchen before letting them eat their creations!). Maybe you've got a big party coming up and you're looking for inspiration – check out the menu plans scattered throughout these pages to take the stress out of the decision-making process!

Whatever your skills as a baker, whatever the size of your oven, here is everything you need to take your first baking steps, or take your baking up a notch with imaginative recipes and great decorating techniques. So grab your apron, preheat the oven and get the eggs, flour, sugar and butter into the mixing bowl!

CONTENTS

The Basics 6

Get the low-down on what you need for successful baking, and how to make do with what you have.

Cookies 10

Perhaps the simplest sweet treats to bake, cookies are a great place to start your baking obsession.

Top Tips 18

So you've made a start in the world of baking, and your results are good but not mind-blowing. Well, read on for expert tips on getting the best out of your oven, your equipment, your ingredients and your recipes!

Cupcakes 22

Such fun to bake, such fun to eat – cupcakes are a delicious everyday treat that keep fresh for a good few days in an airtight container.

Cupcake Decorate! 32

Mastered the baking part? Well let yourself go wild with the frosting and sprinkles!

Party Menus 36

Feeling inspired to bake treats for a party but don't know what to make? Take the stress out of planning with these great party menus!

Classic Cakes 38

Everyone needs a few of the classics in their baking repertoire, and these lovelies won't let you down.

The Frosting on the Cake 48

If you want to make your cakes, cookies or cupcakes extra-special then decorating them is the way forward. Here are simple frostings plus how to use a decorating bag to create professional results.

Teabreads and Loaves   50

Loaf cakes are perfect on picnics and terrific with tea – and what's more they're super-simple to make!

Summer Party Menus   60

Find some great baking combination ideas here for a perfect summer picnic or an elegant garden party.

Knead It!   62

Breadmaking by hand gives wonderful results, but you need to knead the dough in the correct way for best results.

Beautiful Bread   64

Great bread recipes for fantastic artisan loaves.

Sweet and Savoury Muffins   68

The favourite of any more slap-dash cook, muffins taste better if they've been thrown together in a flash. Perfect for when there's not much time to spare!

THE BASICS

You don't need much to bake simple cakes, cookies and muffins: a few basic ingredients, some modest equipment, and an oven. You need to be able to measure out your ingredients accurately with weighing scales or cups, and to be able to follow the instructions in a recipe. And that's all there is to it – simple really!

If you are reading this, it is more than likely that you have a roof over your head and the ability to make a few choices about what you do and don't want to eat. Lucky you and lucky me, quite frankly. This isn't meant to be a lecture, but I do like the idea of making cakes and cookies with a conscience. If you are going be bothered to bake, bake with nice ingredients. I am not saying that everything has to be organic and grown within a 150-foot radius of your dwelling, but why not use good-quality cocoa or unwaxed lemons (who wants to eat a load of wax?). And please, please, please, use free-range eggs. If you'd seen my hens the day they had been rescued from the battery, you'd use free-range eggs, too.

The ingredients used within these pages are pretty straightforward. Most of them can be bought in the supermarket, but anything you can't get there can be found in a health food store. If you can't find decorative frivolities, there are lots of brilliant online shops, which will send you a parcel full of excitement (after you have paid them, of course). These places are also an Aladdin's cave for cookie cutters. Pop what you want into a search engine ('sugar craft suppliers' is a good start) and voilà – a cornucopia of delights.

If you don't have or can't find what you need, try asking friends, family and neighbours. You'll probably find that people are only too happy to lend their baking equipment if they get a few baked goods in return as a thank you!

Butter or margarine

I really think cakes are better made with soft margarine rather than butter. There. I've said it. The world continues to turn and I do believe that the roof hasn't been struck by lightning. Most things are better with butter: pastry, cheese sauce, scones … and I wouldn't want margarine melting onto my crumpet, thank you very much. I just feel that you get a more consistently light sponge with a soft margarine. It's up to you entirely and you'll see recipes for both, but using soft margarine means that you can bung all the ingredients into one bowl and whizz away. It can't get any easier. Cookies, however, are better made with butter – preferably unsalted – and all the recipes here are based on this. Margarine will make them taste foul and the consistency will be wrong. Even that spreadable butter is no good – it's too soft – don't do it.

Using good quality ingredients will make your baking taste even better!

For more straight-talking advice on all things baking, see Kate Shirazi's book

Chocolate

You have probably heard many times before that what you cook will be only as good as the ingredients you use. Silk purse, sow's ear and all that. I have to say that this is very relevant to these recipes, but – you are under no obligation to buy only the finest single estate 72% chocolate, harvested by a man called Eric. Yes, you get what you pay for, but buy what you can afford and whatever strikes you as the best choice at the time. I am sure that a pudding made with single estate chocolate will taste better than a pudding made with cheap chocolate. But unless you are comparing and contrasting the two puddings, the one made with cheap chocolate will still taste good. It just won't be ambrosial. A serious point to consider when buying chocolate is the issue of Fair Trade. Now, I really don't want to rant and make you, dear reader, feel uncomfortable and guilty. We do need to be aware, however, that the business of chocolate is often the cause of hideous injustice for the cacao farmers. There are plenty of Fair Trade chocolate brands available now. These are not difficult to find, and I reckon that the chocolate really does taste better. The finish is generally smoother. Yes, they are more expensive. I am happy to pay the extra because I see chocolate as a treat, not an everyday food, and I'm not thrilled at the thought of the farmer being ripped off. Up to you.

Cocoa

The one ingredient I do get very bossy about is cocoa. Cocoa and drinking chocolate are not the same. If a recipe says cocoa – for goodness' sake, use it. If you use drinking chocolate, you will be adding dried milk powder, sugar, all sorts of weird fats, and salt – and the recipe will not work. The only thing you may substitute for unsweetened cocoa is finely grated 100% cacao, which is utterly fantastic.

Equipment

In terms of kitchen equipment, you don't need anything complicated for baking. Just an oven, some scales, a measuring jug, some measuring spoons, a big bowl and a wooden spoon for mixing, a sieve for sifting, maybe a saucepan for melting or warming, possibly a fork for whisking up any liquid ingredients. And, of course, the right pans.

Happy Hens

Hens are extremely good to us. They lay their eggs and don't make a fuss about it. They don't bite (no teeth), don't howl at the moon, don't go on the rampage scaring old ladies and young children, and don't sit on low walls flicking lit cigarettes at passersby. And what do we do? Cram them into metal cages all piled on top of each other in what I think of as warehouses of doom; then, when they are about 18 months old, ship them off to the fast-food factory. Chicken nugget, anyone? Down the hill from my home is a free-range hen operation. Hundreds and hundreds of brown fluffy-bottomed girls can be seen going about their business (hens are generally very busy creatures), gossiping and scratching around and being naturally hen-like.

Cupcake and muffin cases

For muffins and cupcakes you need a muffin pan and paper cases – I like to use cases for muffins as well as cupcakes as it makes the finished muffins look so much more appealing – and it'll make your washing up so much easier, plus there are the benefits of cases for muffin transportation should you wish to consume muffins outside the home. You can get plain old white papers cases in every supermarket, and many stock pretty patterned ones as well. But it's worth having a search in kitchen shops, too, because it's here that you'll find the best selection of colours and patterns to add a little bit of flair to your baking.

But what size of pan and papers? Muffin pans and cases come in a mind-boggling array of sizes and it would be fair to wonder – which ones should I use? As a general rule, I've used a medium-sized muffin pan for the recipes in this book. Which means the batter quantities are enough for 12 fantastic cupcakes or muffins. So, should you wish to use a muffin pan with larger cups, you'll just end up with fewer cakes, but they'll be a whole lot bigger – and you may need to bake them for a minute or two longer. The only really important thing is to place the cases in a muffin tray before you put the mixture in. If you want to use one of the muffin recipes and cook it in a mini muffin pan – go ahead and just reduce the cooking time accordingly. (You'll also need to halve the recipe quantities – unless you want to make a gazillion muffins!)

You can also find muffin pans in different shapes. My favourite is the heart-shaped muffin pan, which produces the most

gorgeously shaped muffins imaginable. Obviously it's a must for Valentine's Day, but your lover will also adore you for making them heart-shaped muffins any day of the year; a batch for your mother on Mother's Day will make her crumple with pleasure; a plateful for the girls just because they're girls... You see, the possibilities are endless!

Silicone lining

The one bit of kit I think is absolutely critical for the enjoyment of your cookie making experience is re-usable silicone linings. I cannot praise them highly enough and I really wouldn't even consider starting to make a cookie without one on my baking sheet. They are washable and re-usable. I bought a roll of this magic stuff about three years ago and cut it to fit the size of my baking sheets. It's still in action. Sometimes a cursory wipe is even enough if I'm feeling particularly slovenly. Nothing sticks to it. Ever.

Decorating bags

If you choose to undertake some decorating, and I hope you do, may I make a suggestion? Buy a packet of parchment decorating bags. They are small, one-use wonders. By snipping the very end off the bag, you can achieve a fine line of frosting. tips give you a slightly more polished result, that's all. Again, these are available in kitchen and sugarcraft shops everywhere. You really only need three – a couple of fine ones for creating lines and patterns (size 2 and 4) and a chunky star-shaped tip for mountains of buttercream.

> To fill a large decorating bag: turn the edges down and sit it in a mug and it's really easy to plop in the frosting without creating havoc. When filling a small bag, use a teaspoon, or a little palette knife to fill the bag. Only fill the bag a third full, otherwise, when you fold the top over, the frosting squidges out all over your hands

Making do

Pans are an interesting thing in baking. Bear with me, they are. For a long time I possessed only two – one of which was actually a small roasting pan. They did me proud. Of course, when a recipe stated that I must use an 8 in/20 cm loose-bottomed pan, I stared at my choice of two, neither of which could be described as 8 in/ 20 cm or even perfectly round (there was a dropping incident) and each of which had a bottom that was definitely fixed. So, I had educated guesses to make.

This general lack of receptacles taught me some valuable lessons; first, if you have the stated pan, why not use it? But if you haven't, don't panic. Choose the pan that is nearest to the size and make allowances for cooking times. A cake mixture that goes into a smaller pan will take longer to cook. The top may have cremated itself before the middle is done, so you will need to cover it with parchment paper when it starts to look as if it might go horribly wrong. Then it can sit happily for the rest of the cooking time without the top going black. A cake pan that is bigger than suggested in the recipe will result in a flatter cake that will need less cooking time. It's not rocket science. If a recipe asks for two or three sandwich pans, but you've only got one deep round pan, bung it all in and split the cake into three when it is cooked. Only got a round pan and recipe wants square? Shout at the book 'I will not have square cakes in this house!' and put it in the round pan. There will be no knock on the door as the cake-shape police come storming into the kitchen to monitor the situation.

Loose-bottomed pans are useful devils, as are springform pans (especially for cheesecakes). If you're serious about cake-making, it might be worth investing in a range of different-sized round pans, a square pan and a loaf pan. However, I don't want you to start spending loads of money on pans you'll never use, so decide what works best for you. I love a heavy non-stick pan, but, again, it's your choice.

Proper preparation

You'll notice that loads of the recipes ask you to 'grease and line the pan'. At the risk of teaching my grandmother to suck eggs, I shall go through this now. Pans (even the non-stick ones) need to be prepared properly before you bung the mixture in if you ever want your cake to come out in one piece.

Grease the pan first with a dab of butter or margarine, then pop the pan on top of some greaseproof paper and draw round it. Cut out the base and put it to one side. Cut a strip of greaseproof paper into a rectangle as long as the circumference of the pan and ¾ in/2 cm higher than the depth. Fold the ¾ in/2 cm strip upwards and make small snips every ¾ in/2 cm or so up to the fold line. Place the rectangle inside the pan – the cut bits should happily sit along the base of the pan and the paper should stick to the greased sides. Then pop the base piece on top.

Mix it up

A wooden spoon and a valiant thrashing using good old elbow grease are fine up to a point. You are letting yourself in for a workout here and are committing to expending some serious effort. If you're not prepared to work up a sweat, may I suggest the interference of a little electricity? I am a huge fan of the upright mixer. In my world, they cannot be, er, beaten. If you don't have a mixer a food processor works quite well, even though it chops rather than beats. A handheld electric whisk is also useful and I would always choose one of these alternatives over reliance on my delicate arms, a wooden spoon and a lazy nature.

COOKIES

Cookies have got to be one of the simplest things to bake – and are guaranteed to fill your home with a fresh-baked fragrance that'll lure everyone to the kitchen! These fabulous recipes are from Kate Shirazi's book *Cookie Magic*.

Gingerbread gangland

Makes
1
batch

This dough is very easy to make and you don't end up with those hard-as-stone cookies. I implore you to go to town with the decoration. There is room for some minor acts of subversion here – I like to turn the gingerbread boys and girls into really naughty people, sticking their tongues out and forgetting to put their trousers on. Shun the world of currant buttons, embrace the decorating bag and take the road to gingerbread badness...

2⅓ cups/12 oz/340 g all-purpose/plain flour (but you may need more)
1 tsp baking soda/bicarbonate of soda
2 tsp ground ginger
1 stick/4 oz/110 g butter
scant 1 cup/6 oz/175 g soft light brown sugar
1 large free-range egg
4 tbsp corn/golden syrup
4 tbsp royal icing (see p.48)
Food colouring gels
Silver dragées
You will need several parchment paper decorating/piping bags and size 2 tubes/nozzles

1 Sift the flour, baking soda/bicarbonate of soda and ginger into a large bowl. Add the butter and rub it in with your fingertips until you have a mixture resembling fine breadcrumbs. Add the sugar and give it a good mix.

2 In another bowl, beat the egg and corn/golden syrup together. I find a whisk works wonders here. Tip it over the flour mix and stir well. You may find it easier to get your hands in at this point. Sometimes the dough can be a bit on the sticky side. Keep sprinkling over flour and working it in until you have a lovely smooth dough.

3 Wrap the dough in plastic wrap and leave to chill in the refrigerator for at least 30 minutes, but an hour would be better.

4 Preheat the oven to 375°F/190°C/Gas mark 5 and line two baking sheets with silicone liners.

5 Roll the dough out on a lightly floured surface to a thickness of about ¼ inch/4 mm. Cut out the required shapes, place them slightly apart on your lined baking sheets and bake for 12–15 minutes until golden. Leave to cool slightly on the baking sheets before transferring them to a wire rack to cool completely. To decorate, divide the icing into as many colours as you want and tint with the gels. Place a dot of icing in each decorating bag and pipe away to your heart's content. I like to pipe 2 dots for eyes and place the silver dragées on top. Leave them to dry before showing them to people and laughing loudly.

Lemon cookies

I think lemon and almond go particularly well together. These are really easy to make and as an added extra, don't even need rolling out. They are also very versatile. If you don't want lemony ones (how odd), omit the zest and add whatever jam takes your fancy.

½ cup/ 4 oz/110 g superfine/caster sugar
scant 2 sticks/7½ oz/210 g butter, softened
½ cup/2 oz/60 g confectioners'/ icing sugar
1 large free-range egg yolk
1½ cups/5 oz/150 g ground almonds
1 tsp almond extract
Finely grated zest and juice of 1 large unwaxed lemon
2 cups/10 oz/300 g all-purpose/ plain flour
1 tsp baking powder
1 x small jar of lemon curd (you'll need about ⅓ cup/4½ oz/ 120 g or so)

1　Preheat the oven to 375°F/190°C/ Gas mark 5 and line two baking sheets with silicone liners.

2　Beat the superfine/caster sugar and butter together in a large bowl until very pale and fluffy. Beat in the confectioners'/icing sugar, egg yolk, ground almonds, almond extract, zest and 2 tsp of the lemon juice. Give it a good thrashing. Sift in the flour and baking powder and stir until everything is combined.

3　Form a blob of the mixture into a ball just a bit smaller than a golf ball and place on your lined baking sheets. Keep going, leaving a space between all your golf balls. With your thumb, squish down to form a little well in the now flattened ball and fill with a little dollop of lemon curd (not too much or it will overflow and burn). Bake for about 10–12 minutes until the cookies are golden and gorgeous.

4　Transfer to a wire rack to cool.

WARNING
Don't be greedy and
eat them while warm –
the lemon curd will
still be molten hot.

Makes
1
batch

Ginger cookies

These are the unsophisticated, gorgeously moreish cookies that positively reek of ground ginger and which are very popular with both children and adults. A cookie with no drawbacks as far as I am concerned.

1 cup/5 oz/150 g self-rising/-raising flour
½ tsp baking soda/bicarbonate of soda
2 tsp ground ginger
1 tsp ground cinnamon
2 tsp superfine/caster sugar
½ stick/ 2 oz/60 g butter
2 tbsp corn/golden syrup

1   Preheat the oven to 375°F/190°C/ Gas mark 5 and line two baking sheets with silicone liners.

2   Sift together all the dry ingredients in a large bowl. Heat the butter and corn/golden syrup gently in a pan and when the butter has melted, pour it over the dry ingredients. Mix well until you have a soft dough. If it's a little bit sticky, sprinkle a little more flour onto it until you get a consistency you can comfortably handle.

3   Using your hands, form small balls of the mixture, flatten them slightly and place them on your lined baking sheets, allowing a little space between them as they spread. Bake for about 15 minutes until golden and gorgeous-looking.

4   Let the cookies cool and harden on the baking sheets for a bit before lifting them onto wire racks to cool completely.

Chocolate chip shortbread

This is a really easy peasy way of jazzing up shortbread.

Makes
1
batch

1¼ sticks/9 oz/250 g butter, softened,
¼ cup/2 oz/60 g superfine/caster sugar
1¾ cups/9 oz/250 g all-purpose/plain flour
scant 1 cup/4½ oz/125 g cornstarch/
cornflour
¼ cup/2 oz/60 g chunky chocolate chips

1 Cream the butter and sugar together in a large bowl until pale and fluffy. Sift the flour and cornstarch/cornflour onto the butter mixture and mix until you have a lovely smooth dough.

2 Sprinkle the chocolate chips over the dough and knead in with your lovely clean hands until the chocolate is evenly distributed.

3 Roll out a sheet of plastic wrap, tip the dough onto it, then form the dough into a fat sausage and wrap up tightly. Leave to chill in the refrigerator for at least an hour.

4 Preheat the oven to 325°F/170°C/ Gas mark 3 and line two baking sheets with silicone liners.

5 Remove the roll of dough from its plastic wrap and slice into circles. Place the circles on your lined baking sheets and bake for about 30 minutes until they are pale golden. Leave the shortbread to cool on wire racks.

TOP TIPS

Ovens and their vagaries are always a bit of a nightmare when it comes to writing recipes. Even if we all had the same make and model of oven, I would bet that they would all cook slightly differently. So, bearing in mind that some of us have fan ovens, some have gas, some have Agas, some have snazzy and some have basic, there is no way that if a recipe says 'bakes in 20 minutes' you can take that as the law.

In baking there is an element of using your own judgement as well as following a recipe. Have a peep at the cake at least 5 minutes before the end of the allotted time and see whether it's time to a) retrieve it; b) cover it with a bit of greaseproof paper to prevent the top burning and give it another 10 minutes; or c) just to leave it another 5 minutes. It's a judgement call – yours. A cake is generally done when a sharp knife or skewer stuck into it comes back clean without any globs of raw cake mixture sticking to it. It should be firm to the touch, and in the case of a sponge, have a bit of a spring to it when you give it a mild poke. Finger sinking into the midst – not good. Being able to rap your knuckles on the top of a carbonated surface – also not good.

So, you've followed all the instructions and something has still gone wrong. Here follows a small compendium of what might have caused the problem and, ultimately, how to wriggle your way out of it.

Never admit that the cake you present with a flourish is not what you had first envisaged. A cake is a wonderful thing, full stop. No one need ever know, and only a very mean-spirited person would comment negatively about a cake that someone else has made. In fact, take the cake away from them – they don't deserve it. They can watch other people eat it. That'll teach them.

Storage

How long do cakes, cookies and muffins keep? It really depends on how you store them. Real cakes and cookies go stale quicker than shop-bought ones. I reckon on a good four or five days in a biscuit tin with a tight lid. I bet they don't hang around for that long though… Muffins are much, much better when they're freshly made, so you really, honestly do have to eat them on the day you make them. Personally, I'm a little bit brutal about these things – muffins are an indulgence, and where's the indulgent luxury in something that's not at its absolute best? So go on, dig in and gobble them up as quickly as you can!

Troubleshooting tips

- If your cake is solid and brick-like, it might be for a couple of reasons: you may not have beaten enough air into the mixture (did you use a wooden spoon and come over all weak?), or if the recipe required you to fold in the flour, you may have been a bit too vigorous and bashed all the air out of your batter.

- If your cake is a bit dry and crumbly, the mixture might have been too stiff and dry and the oven temperature may have been a little on the high side. Next time, lower the oven temperature and add a splash of milk to the batter.

- If the fruit sinks to the bottom of your cake, it's generally because it's too damp or sticky. I always rinse and dry candied cherries. The mixture may have been a bit too soft to carry the fruit as it rises.

- A cake that's sinking in the middle may be due to a couple of reasons: there may have been too much raising agent, or too soft a mixture. Check the oven temperature, too. An oven that is too hot or too cool can cause a cake to sink.

- Don't chuck out a cake because of its texture. If it is inedible as a cake, make it into cake crumbs and freeze them – there are loads of uses for cake crumbs in other recipes and it's handy to have a stash tucked away. If the cake is flat and tragic, use a cutter to cut out shapes and sandwich them together with jam or buttercream.

- With a cake that has risen unevenly, just level the top, turn it upside down and ice the bottom.

- A cake with a massively sunken middle can be turned into a mega pudding; cut out the centre and pile whipped cream and fruit into the hole. A dusting of confectioners' sugar, and voilà!

Oven tips

Now it may seem obvious, but try to use your common sense when you're baking. Every oven is different and has its own special foibles. Some ovens cook slightly quicker, some slightly slower. Some ovens have 'hot patches' so you'll need to turn the tray to prevent half your cakes or biscuits browning more than the other half. So, all ovens cook differently, and I don't want to be responsible for your burnt or raw cakes. Cakes are done if they are firm to the touch and a bit springy on top. You can also insert a toothpick into the centre – if it comes out clean, the cake is done.

If you don't trust your oven's temperature gauge, invest in a separate oven thermometer

Muffin tips

I'd like to pretend there's a huge amount of skill and talent involved in baking a batch of golden-brown, sweetly scented muffins – but I'm afraid I'd be lying. They are so unbelievably easy-peasy to make, pretty much anyone can do it – even self-professed failures in the kitchen. But there are a few secrets to making really light fluffy muffins that differ from cakes and cookies – see in particular point three below (which may well appeal directly to the more slapdash cooks among us).

Number 1: To make a sweeping generalization – combine your dry ingredients, combine your wet ingredients, put the two together and bingo: 12 muffins! But before you get to this stage, there's a golden rule...

Number 2: Even if this seems like a pain do it anyway! Sift all your dry ingredients together before you add the wet ingredients. You want your flour, sugar, cocoa, etc. to be as light as air, filling your mixing bowl in soft drifts like freshly fallen snow.

Number 3: Once you add the wet ingredients, don't over-mix! The temptation will be to give the batter a good old beating to make sure you've got a lovely smooth mixture. But this is wrong, wrong, wrong. Give it a gentle, brief stir – just enough to combine the ingredients, but no more than that. The average muffin mixture will still look a bit lumpy and chunky, and if you've still got a few streaks of flour – don't worry about it. Just scoop up big spoonfuls of the mixture, dollop them into the cases, then bung the tray in the oven. Twenty minutes later you'll be in heaven and wondering why you don't make these gorgeous creations every morning.

And if you don't follow this advice? Well, they'll still be edible, but your muffins won't have that fabulously fluffy texture that all the best muffins should have. They'll be a little tough, a little bit more solid than you'd like. So take my advice and always give your muffins the quick 1-2-3 treatment.

Melting chocolate tips

A word here is needed about melting chocolate. There are two methods of melting chocolate (three, if you count giving it to a child to hold in the back of a car). The first is the safest! Place the chopped-up chocolate in a heatproof bowl over a pan of barely simmering water. The crucial thing here is that the bottom of the bowl must not touch the water; the chocolate gets too hot. Nightmare: grainy ghastly mess; straight in the bin; tears. Don't do it.

The second method is quicker, more gung-ho, and I like to think of it as the rapid assault method of melting chocolate. Quick, brutal – but not without risk: the microwave. Put the chopped chocolate into a microwaveable container, then zap it. Do short bursts of only 10–15 seconds and stir between each zapping. I recommend you stop while there are still some lumps and just keep stirring – the residual heat will melt the rest. The danger here is going for the burn (especially with white chocolate): one second, it is fine and dandy and thoroughly enjoying its little warm-up; the next second, Whoa! All gone horribly, horribly wrong. Have you ever tasted burnt chocolate? Nasty.

Batches of cookies

Now we need to have a full and frank discussion about how many cookies each recipe makes. Most recipe books have a little bit saying 'makes 24 cookies' or something similar. Each recipe here will make one batch – a do-able, edible batch. You shouldn't have so few as to make it not worthwhile and you shouldn't have too many so you are eating them for weeks. The problem with stating numbers is that I positively want you to use different sorts of cutters. How the devil do you work out how many cookies would be made using a heart-shaped cutter, if someone decides to use a giant T-Rex cutter? If you roll the dough two more times than me, you'll have a thinner cookie and you'll get more. Do you see my point? My small teaspoon is going to be different from your small teaspoon. Embrace the unknown, just make the cookies and enjoy them – don't let yourself get hung up on the fact that a recipe says 'makes 24' and you've got 12 – or 45.

Most types of cookie dough freeze well for up to a month if you wrap them carefully in parchment paper and plastic wrap, so if a recipe makes what looks like too much, simply freeze half for another occasion.

CUPCAKES

Everyone loves a cupcake – dainty, moreish and oh so pretty. Taken from Kate Shirazi's book *Cupcake Magic*, the following recipes are sure to have your friends and family begging for more!

Carrot cupcakes
with honey orange cream cheese frosting

Makes about 10

There are so many recipes for carrot cake around that I'd say, if you have a favourite one, try it in cupcake liners. This is my favourite – one of those recipes on a scrappy bit of paper tucked into my collection. I like the fact that the frosting contains no sugar, being sweetened with honey. One thing I would suggest – use only proper cream cheese – sometimes sold as curd cheese. I've never had much success with the white soft cheese sold in supermarkets everywhere. It's too runny.

Generous ¾ cup/6 oz/175 g soft brown sugar
¾ cup/6 fl oz/175 ml sunflower oil
3 large free-range eggs
1 cup/5 oz/150 g all-purpose/plain flour
1½ tsp baking soda/bicarbonate of soda
1½ tsp baking powder
1 tsp ground cinnamon
½ tsp freshly grated nutmeg
A pinch of salt
2 cups/8 oz/225 g grated or shredded carrot

FOR THE CREAM CHEESE FROSTING
1 x 8 oz/225 g packet curd/cream cheese (not soft or light cream cheese), softened
2 tsp honey (or more to taste)
Grated zest of 1 unwaxed orange
Orange sprinkles to decorate

1   Preheat the oven to 350°F/180°C/ Gas mark 4. Line a 12-hole muffin pan/tin with cupcake liners/cases. Mix the sugar and oil in a large bowl. Add the eggs and mix well. Sift in the dry ingredients, and beat everything together until really well combined. Next add the grated carrots and stir through well.

2   Place spoonfuls of batter in the prepared cases, and bake in the oven for 15–20 minutes. Watch these like a hawk, as they have a tendency to burn. If the tops are getting a bit dark and it looks like the innards are still raw, cover with parchment paper, and cook a little longer. Remove from the oven and leave to cool.

3   While they are cooling, make the frosting. Put the cream cheese in a bowl, and beat until softened. Stir in the honey and orange zest. Give it a taste to make sure it is sweet enough. Add a bit more honey if you want. When the cakes are cold, spread the frosting over the top and decorate at will.

Battenburg cupcakes

I love the colour combination of Battenburg and toyed with the idea of wrapping the whole caboodle in marzipan, but I settled on this version. I like the tang of the apricot jam, but you could use any other flavour. You don't have to stick to pink sponge, either. Why not green and blue?

1²/₃ cups/8 oz/225 g self-rising/-raising flour

1 cup/8 oz/225 g superfine/caster sugar

1 cup/8 oz/225 g margarine, softened

2 tsp baking powder

4 large free-range eggs

2 tsp pure vanilla extract

Pink food colouring (preferably gel)

Apricot jam for spreading

1 quantity lemon glacé frosting (p.48)

Dolly mixture or other sprinkles to decorate

1 Preheat oven to 325°F/160°C/Gas mark 3. Grease two 8 in/20 cm square cake pans/tins, and line with baking parchment.

2 Sift the flour and sugar into a mixing bowl, food processor or food mixer. Add the margarine, baking powder, eggs and vanilla. Beat until light and fluffy. Divide the batter into two equal portions in separate bowls, and add a little bit of pink food colouring to one half. Pour each cake mixture into a separate tin, and bake in the oven for 20–25 minutes until firm to the touch and golden. Don't worry that the pink cake doesn't look very pink. Remove from the oven and turn both cakes onto wire racks to cool.

3 Using a sharp knife, level the tops of the cakes so that the top and the bottom are completely flat. Spread a thin layer of apricot jam over the upper side of the pink layer. Place the plain cake on top so that the bottom side of the sponge faces upwards. Cut into ¾ in/2 cm strips.

4 Now, pay attention. Lay one strip on its side so that you have a line of pink and a line of yellow. Spread a thin layer of jam over the top. Take another strip of cake and lay it on its side on top of the jammy strip, but reversed so that yellow lies directly on top of pink and vice versa. Cut these strips into squares, and drizzle with the glacé frosting. Let some of the frosting dribble down the sides. Plop a dolly mixture (or alternative adornment) on top, and place in cupcake liners.

Bite my cherry

Yes, yes, this is my version of the cherry Bakewell tart, one of my all-time favourite cakes. But, get this – no fat, no flour and contains fruit and nuts. Not only is it perfectly wonderful for gluten-intolerant personages, but also it must somehow count as 'good for you'. Surely?

4 large free-range eggs, separated
¾ cup/6 oz/175 g superfine/caster sugar
2¼ cups/8 oz/225 g ground almonds
1 tsp baking powder (or ½ tsp baking
soda/bicarbonate of soda and
1 tsp cream of tartar if you want to keep
it gluten-free)
12 candied cherries

FOR THE DECORATION
1 quantity lemon glacé frosting (p.48)
Golf-ball-sized piece of sugar paste
(rolled fondant)
Red food colouring (preferably gel)
edible glue
Red edible glitter
Green food colouring (preferably gel)
1 tbsp royal icing (see p.48)
You will need a parchment decorating/
piping bag

1 Preheat the oven to 400°F/200°C/ Gas mark 6. Line a 12-hole muffin pan/tin with cupcake liners/cases.

2 Beat the egg yolks and sugar together until pale. In a clean, dry separate bowl, whisk the egg whites until stiff peaks form. Gently fold them into the egg yolk mixture, then fold in the ground almonds and baking powder. Spoon the batter into the prepared cases, and push 1 cherry down into each sponge. Bake in the oven for 15–20 minutes, keeping an eye on them throughout – burnt almond doesn't taste good. Remove from the oven and leave to cool.

3 Make a glacé frosting (p.16) and pour a little over each cake. While you are waiting for the frosting to set (30 minutes), make the sugar paste cherries. Dye the sugar paste red by dipping a toothpick/cocktail stick into the red food colouring and transferring it to the paste. Knead the colour in evenly, then make little cherry-sized balls (one for each cupcake), paint them with the edible glue and roll them in the edible glitter.

4 When the frosting is dry, add a little food colouring to the royal icing to make it green. Fill a parchment decorating/piping bag with the royal icing, squeezing down to the end. Snip the very end off the bag. Stick a sugar paste cherry onto each cupcake with a tiny blob of edible glue, and pipe green stalks and leaves with the green royal icing.

Crushed Pineapple 20 oz

Sour Cream 8 oz

2 pk Vanilla instant pudding Mix

Digestive Biscuits + butter
or base

Whipped cream pineapple
+ cherries to decorate

Chirpy chirpy cheep cheep

I love those little fluffy yellow chicks that appear in shops just before Easter. If you don't want to do anything other than ice some cupcakes, you could stand one of these chicks on top. Just make sure that no one thinks that they are edible. Otherwise these simple piped chicks look very lovely. Pastel colours really do look better here.

Generous ¾ cup/4 oz/110 g self-rising/
-raising flour, sifted
½ cup/4 oz/110 g superfine/caster sugar,
sifted
½ cup/4 oz/110 g margarine, softened
1 tsp baking powder
2 large free-range eggs
1 tsp pure vanilla extract

FOR THE DECORATION
1 quantity of glacé frosting (see p.48)
tinted in pastel colours with gel food
colouring
2 tbsp royal icing (see p.48) plus 1 tbsp
green royal icing (optional) yellow,
black and orange gel food colouring
You will need 3 decorating/piping bags
with fine tubes/nozzles

1 Preheat the oven to 325°F/160°C/Gas mark 3. Line a 12-hole muffin pan/tin with baking cups/cupcake cases. Put all the ingredients (except the icing and sprinkles) in a mixer (food processor, food mixer, or just a big bowl with an electric whisk). Mix really well until the batter is light and fluffy. Put heaped teaspoons of the mixture into the prepared cases, and bake in the oven for about 20 minutes until golden, and firm and springy when you give them a light prod on top. Let them cool before preparing the icing – on a wire rack if you want, but not 100 per cent necessary.

2 Make the cupcakes and leave them to cool. Ice the cooled cupcakes with a selection of pastel-coloured icings in glacé or fondant. Leave them to dry.

3 Split the royal icing into thirds. Take two-thirds and tint it yellow with gel food colouring. Fill a decorating/piping bag with the yellow icing, and push to the end. To make a fluffy chick, pipe a chick shape onto the cake, and fill in the chick with random squiggles of yellow icing. Make sure that you go ever so slightly over your outline, so that the chick looks really fluffy. To make a flatter chick, again pipe an outline. Thin out some of the yellow royal icing with a few drops of water so that you have a consistency a bit thicker than heavy/double cream. Carefully fill in the outline with this mixture, and leave to dry completely.

4 When both are dry, divide the remaining royal icing into two, and tint one portion black and the other orange. Fill two separate decorating bags, one with the black and one with the orange. Pipe an eye on each chick (two if the chick is not in profile!) with the black icing, and a beak with the orange.

5 If you have any extra royal icing, tint it another colour (green looks good), and pipe tiny spots all the way round the outer edge of the cupcakes.

Zucchini, feta & scallion cupcakes

The great hunks of feta in these cupcakes are a lovely surprise. The zucchini adds moisture and flavour, as well as beautiful flecks of green. These go well with a really piquant salsa. The batter is very stiff, almost dough-like. Don't worry and don't add more milk. The zucchini sorts out the texture. Have faith.

scant 1½ cups/7 oz/200 g all-purpose/
plain flour
2 tbsp sugar
3 tsp baking powder
½ tsp salt
1 small zucchini/courgette, grated
2 scallions/spring onions, finely chopped
1 cup/8 oz/225 g ricotta cheese
5 oz/150 g feta cheese, crumbled
into chunks
2 large free-range eggs, lightly beaten
½ cup/4 oz/110 g butter, melted
¼ cup/2 fl oz/60 ml milk

1　Preheat the oven to 400°F/200°C/
Gas mark 6. Line a 12-hole muffin
pan/tin with cupcake liners/cases.

2　Sift the flour, sugar, baking powder
and salt into a large bowl, and mix
through well. In another bowl, mix
the zucchini/courgette, scallions/
spring onions, ricotta, feta, eggs,
melted butter and the milk. Give it
a bit of a beat around, then add to
the dry ingredients. The batter will
be stiff. Spoon the mixture into the
prepared cases, take the worried
look off your face and put them
in the oven. Bake in the oven for
20–25 minutes or until firm to the
touch and golden brown. Eat warm.

CUPCAKE DECORATE!

Who needs an excuse to bake something scrumptious? Whether it's Valentine's Day, Mother's Day or a Batchelorette party, Cakeadoodle Doo's Kate Shirazi has an incredible edible creation for any occasion.

CUPCAKE BASE RECIPE

Generous ¾ cup/4 oz/110 g self-rising/-raising flour, sifted
½ cup/4 oz/110 g superfine/caster sugar, sifted
½ cup/4 oz/110 g margarine, softened
1 tsp baking powder
2 large free-range eggs
1 tsp pure vanilla extract

Preheat the oven to 325°F/160°C/Gas mark 3. Line a 12-hole muffin pan/tin with baking cups/cupcake cases. Put all the ingredients in a mixer (food processor, food mixer, or just a big bowl with an electric whisk).

Mix really well until the batter is light and fluffy. Put heaped teaspoons of the batter into the prepared cases, and bake in the oven for about 20 minutes until golden, and firm and springy when you give them a light prod on top. Let them cool before preparing the icing – on a wire rack if you want, but not 100 per cent necessary.

English summer cupcakes

This recipe works really well as a dessert after a lovely summery lunch. This is another of those recipes that can look very elegant, but is very easy.

1½ cups/9 oz/250 g mascarpone cheese
Selection of soft ripe fruit such as blueberries, strawberries, raspberries, peaches and nectarines

Empty the tub of mascarpone cheese into a bowl and give it a bit of a beating, but don't add anything to it. Place a dollop of mascarpone on top of each of the cupcakes, and artfully arrange the fruit on and around the cakes.

Mother's Day delights

You can buy pre-made sugar roses in most specialist cake decorating stores and on websites if you are pushed for time. Whatever you decide, these cupcakes will make a spectacular treat for Mother's Day.

1¾ cups/7 oz/200 g confectioners'/icing sugar, sifted
Boiling water
Gel food colouring
12 candied/sugared roses

To make the icing, put the confectioners'/icing sugar in a bowl, and slowly add boiling water until you have a thick soup consistency. Add the food colouring and pour over cakes. Wait about 10 minutes before carefully placing a rose on top of each cupcake.

1 CUPCAKE 3 GREAT IDEAS!
Use the cupcake base recipe and follow these simple instruction for three different looks!

Batchelorette party

These kinky cakes are guaranteed to get the party started. So let the fun begin, gals!

1 quantity of glacé frosting (see p.48)
2 tbsp royal icing (see p.48)
Dark brown and pink gel food coloring

Ice your cooled cupcakes with pale pink glacé frosting. Leave to dry for at least 1 hour. Tint half the royal icing dark brown. If it gets too runny, add some more sifted confectioners'/icing sugar. Put the brown icing in a decorating bag with a fine tube and the remaining white royal icing into another one.

With the brown icing, pipe 1950-style dresses onto a few cakes (small waists, big skirts), high heeled shoes on a few more and handbags onto yet more. If you are stuck for ideas, look in a few magazines or draw out a few examples first. Fill in patterns and folds on the dresses, buckles and pockets on the bags, and stitch lines and other details on the shoes with the white icing. Make them as cheeky as you dare!

Halloween super scaries

It's the time of year to roast some squash or pumpkin and then throw it into these irresistibly sweet and spicy muffins. Look out for fake spiders and other nasties in kids' toy shops and hide a few on the plate to scare anyone else away ... leaving you with a big batch of muffins all to yourself!

Makes 12

7 oz/200 g peeled, seeded pumpkin, cut into chunks
½ tbsp sunflower oil
2 cups/10 oz/300 g all-purpose/plain flour
1 tbsp baking powder
1 tsp ground cinnamon
1 egg, beaten
Scant ⅔ cup/5 fl oz/150 ml sour cream
Scant/¼ cup/50 ml/1¾ fl oz milk
½ cup/4 oz/115 g soft brown sugar
¼ cup/ 2 oz/60 g butter, melted

TO DECORATE
5 oz/150 g white chocolate
1 oz/25 g bittersweet/dark chocolate

Preheat the oven to 375°F/190°C/Gas mark 5. Put the pumpkin in a baking dish, drizzle with the oil, then toss to coat. Roast for about 35 minutes until tender. Remove from the oven and leave to cool, then mash roughly with a fork.

To make the muffins, preheat the oven to 400°F/200°C/Gas mark 6. Grease or line a 12-hole muffin pan/tin. Combine the flour, baking powder and cinnamon and sift into a large bowl. In a separate bowl, combine the egg, sour cream, milk, mashed squash, sugar and butter and stir together until well mixed. Pour into the dry ingredients and stir together until just combined, then spoon large dollops of the mixture into the prepared muffin pan.

Bake for about 20 minutes until risen and golden. Leave to cool in the pan for a few minutes, then transfer to a wire rack.

To decorate, melt the white chocolate in a heatproof bowl set over a pan of barely simmering water, then spoon on top of the cakes. Melt the bittersweet/dark chocolate in the same way in a separate bowl, then spoon into a decorating bag/piping with a very narrow tube/nozzle. Pipe concentric circles onto each cake, then use a skewer to draw a line from the centre to the outside of each cake to make a spider's web pattern.

Gadzooks for the spooks

Black Halloween cupcakes are highly entertaining. Black frosting is wonderful – it transforms your teeth and mouth at first bite. There is absolutely no room for subtlety here. You can scare the living daylights out of trick-or-treaters, by having a mouthful of cake just before you open the door. Rest assured that the colour does fade quite rapidly...

Makes about 12

1 quantity of basic cupcakes (see p.32)
1 quantity of glacé frosting (see p.48)
Black and orange food colouring (preferably gel)
Golf ball-sized piece of rolled fondant/sugar paste
Edible glue
You will need a small paintbrush

Make the cupcakes and allow to cool. Make up the glacé frosting, and divide into two portions; use the food colouring to make one black and the other deep orange. Divide the cupcakes into two batches, and ice one batch black and the other batch orange. Leave them to dry. (These cakes need to be completely dry before you add anything else because of the dark colours.)

Take a third of the rolled fondant and tint it black. Make a ghost by flattening out a piece of white sugar paste into the shape of a ghost and use edible glue to stick it onto a black-iced cupcake. Let the ghost trail over the edge of the cake in a ghostly manner. Take some tiny bits of black paste, and stick them on to make a ghoulish face for the ghost.

Make the spider by taking a bit of black paste the size of a fava/broad bean, and sticking it onto an orange-iced cake using edible glue. Make as many legs as you can (8 is traditional!) out of slivers of black paste, and stick them on. I also like to add a final strip of black for the web. A face and fangs made out of white rolled fondant finishes it off.

For the spooky eyes, take 2 elongated egg shapes of white rolled fondant, add black pupils and stick onto a black-iced cake.

Easy-peasy heart cupcakes

Yes, there is some piping here. No, it isn't tricky. Royal icing is invaluable for piping. You can use it for frosting cakes if you like a very hard surface. What I suggest you do if you are a bit nervous about your piping skills is to practice on a plate or directly onto your work surface. When you are happy that you have the flow of the shape right, go for it! Let the base layer of frosting dry really well before you start decorating. If you want to create something other than hearts, do it. Tiny spots all over look really pretty and couldn't be simpler.

Makes around 12

1 quantity of basic cupcakes (see p.32)
1 quantity of glacé frosting (see p.48)
2 tbsp royal icing (see p.48)
Food colourings (preferably gel)
You will need a parchment decorating/piping bag

Make the cupcakes as for the recipe on p.32, and allow them to cool.

To make the glacé frosting, sift the confectioners'/icing sugar into a bowl, and add the water drop by drop until you get the consistency you require (thick soup). Add the food colouring, and check that you still have the correct consistency – you may need to add a little more sifted confectioners' sugar. Spoon the frosting over the cakes and leave to dry. Leaving them for a couple of hours at this stage is really good, if you can.

Tint the royal icing with the food colouring, then use some to fill the parchment decorating/piping bag, squeezing the icing down to the end.

Snip the very end off the bag. Practice piping the hearts or whatever shape you want, then pipe away to your heart's content on the top of each iced cupcake. Leave to dry for another hour or two before eating.

Easter muffins

When you're celebrating Easter with a gluten- or dairy-intolerant muffin-eater, this is the recipe to choose. Inspired by the fruity marzipan simnel cake, these little muffins look cuter than cute topped off with baby chick yellow frosting and pastel-coloured eggs. Be sure to check the ingredients on your pastel-coloured eggs and marzipan to make sure they don't contain any dairy or gluten.

Makes 12

1½ cups/7 oz/200 g potato flour
²⁄₃ cup/3½ oz/100 g rice flour
1 tbsp cornstarch/cornflour
1 tbsp gluten-free baking powder
Scant ½ cup/3½ oz/100 g superfine/caster sugar
²⁄₃ cup/3½ oz/100 g raisins or golden raisins
2 tbsp candied peel
1 egg, beaten
¾ cup/6 fl oz/175 ml soya milk
6 tbsp sunflower oil
3½ oz/100 g gluten-free marzipan, finely grated
Finely grated zest of 1 lemon

TO DECORATE
1¾ cups/7 oz/200 g confectioners'/icing sugar, sifted
2 tbsp lemon juice
Yellow food colouring
Pastel-coloured mini eggs

Preheat the oven to 400°F/200°C/Gas mark 6. Grease or line a 12-hole muffin pan/tin.

Combine the flours, baking powder and superfine/caster sugar and sift into a large bowl, then add the raisins or golden raisins and candied peel.

In a separate bowl or jug, combine the egg, milk and oil, then stir in the marzipan and lemon zest. Pour into the dry ingredients and stir together until just combined, then spoon large dollops of the mixture into the prepared muffin pan.

Bake for about 20 minutes until risen and golden. Leave to cool in the pan for a few minutes, then transfer to a wire rack to cool.

To decorate, mix the confectioners'/icing sugar and lemon juice until smooth, then add a few drops of food colouring to make a pale yellow frosting. Spoon on top of the cakes and top with mini eggs.

PARTY MENUS

Get the girls round for a relaxing evening and treat everyone to some delicious home-baked treats, and remember that birthday fun isn't just for kids. Get those candles out and make sure everyone sings!

Girls' Night In

Chili Cornmeal Muffins   84

---

98   Upside Down Polenta Plum Cake

Soft Berry Cookies   107

---

26   Cherry Cupcakes

Don't forget to chill some drinks and send the boys out for the evening before they eat all the cakes!

Grown-up Birthday Party

Turn to the recipe pages for full baking instructions.

Sweet treats aren't for everyone – but you could always include one of the savoury muffin recipes on pages 78–87 as well.

CLASSIC CAKES

There is something decadent about producing a whole cake for people to share. Cutting the slices makes having cake somehow more of an occasion than cookies or cupcakes. These classic recipes are from Kate Shirazi's wonderful book *Cake Magic*.

Victoria sponge

Serves
8

Aaah. The mother of all everyday cakes. It is like the comforting, delicious faithful friend of the cake world. The house smells gorgeous when it's in the oven, it's a doddle to make and you can vary it by changing the jam in the middle, adding buttercream, fresh cream, luscious strawberries or raspberries when they are at their best – the possibilities are endless. Victoria sponge, we salute you.

1¼ cups/6 oz/175 g self-rising/-raising flour, sifted
¾ cup/6 oz/175 g superfine/caster sugar
¾ cup/6 oz/175 g soft margarine
3 large free-range eggs
1 tsp vanilla extract
1 tbsp strawberry jam
Confectioners'/icing sugar for dusting

1 Preheat the oven to 325°F/160°C/ Gas mark 3. Grease and line two 8 in/20 cm round sandwich pans/ tins. Put all the ingredients except the jam and the confectioners'/ icing sugar in a large bowl and beat the living daylights out of them. The preferred method is in a freestanding mixer, but you could use an electric hand whisk.

2 When the batter is very pale, fluffy and almost mousse-like, divide it between the prepared pans and smooth out. Bake for about 20 minutes. The cakes should be springy to the touch and a skewer or sharp knife should come out clean when poked into the sponge.

3 Cool the cakes on a wire rack. When they are cold, sandwich them together with the jam, and dust the top with confectioners' sugar. Voilà!

Everyday coffee cake

I love coffee cake. So scrumptious. The key is to add enough coffee. If you're going to have coffee cake, it really should taste of coffee, don't you think? The walnuts on top are optional – as is the icing. You could increase the amount of buttercream and put that on top of the cake, if you wish. Alternatively, leave it naked. Radical.

1¼ cups/6 oz/175 g self-rising/-raising flour, sifted
¾ cup/6 oz/175 g superfine/caster sugar
¾ cup/6 oz/175 g soft margarine
3 large free-range eggs
8 heaped tsp instant coffee granules
3 tsp boiling water
Scant ¾ stick plus 1 tbsp/2½ oz/75 g unsalted butter
2½ cups/10 oz/300 g confectioners'/icing sugar, sifted
8 walnut halves

1 Preheat the oven to 325°F/160°C/Gas mark 3. Grease and line two 8 in/20 cm round sandwich pans/tins. In a mixer, beat together the flour, superfine/caster sugar, margarine and eggs until they are very pale and fluffy.

2 Put the coffee granules in a cup or small bowl and add about 3 tsp boiling water. The coffee should be very, very dark and just runny – if it's a bit stiff, add a few drops more water, but it certainly shouldn't look like ordinary coffee. You want a liquor that will give a huge hit of coffee without having to add too much volume of liquid.

3 Add 1 tsp coffee mixture to the cake mix and beat it in. Have a taste, and add more coffee if you think it needs it. Don't throw away any remaining mixture!

4 Divide the batter between the two pans and smooth out. Bake for about 20 minutes until the cakes are firm and springy to the touch. Cool the cakes on a wire rack while you crack on with the filling and icing.

5 Beat the butter and 1 cup plus 2 tbsp/5 oz/150 g confectioners'/icing sugar together until pale and soft. Add 1 tsp coffee mixture and taste. If the balance is fine, leave it there, but you may wish to add a little more.

6 In another bowl, add the remaining coffee mixture to the remaining confectioners' sugar and mix until you have a smooth mixture with the consistency of custard. If it's too runny, add more confectioners' sugar; if too thick, add a drop of water.

7 When the sponges are cold, sandwich them together with the buttercream and then frost the top of the cake with the coffee frosting. Place the walnuts around the edge of the cake and leave the icing to set, which should only take about an hour or so.

Serves
8

Basic chocolate cake

OK, calling a chocolate cake 'basic' might be a bit off-putting, but this is a no-nonsense chocolate sponge sandwich. It is what it is. There's no getting away from it, but it's a cake that is ultimately very yummy and very few people will turn their noses up at the offer of a slice. The crucial thing that makes this cake great rather than OK is the quality of the cocoa you use. Do not, under any circumstances, use drinking chocolate.

1 cup/5 oz/150 g self-rising/-raising flour, sifted
¾ cup/6 oz/175 g superfine/caster sugar
¾ cup/6 oz/175 g soft margarine
3 large free-range eggs
1 tbsp milk
Scant ½ cup/1¾ oz/50 g cocoa powder, sifted
Scant 1 stick/3½ oz/100 g unsalted butter
1¾ cups/7 oz/200 g confectioners'/icing sugar, sifted
1–2 tsp milk (optional)
Chocolate buttons to decorate (optional)

1   Preheat the oven to 325°F/160°C/ Gas mark 3. Grease and line two 8 in/20 cm round sandwich pans/ tins. In a mixer (preferably), beat together the flour, superfine/caster sugar, margarine, eggs, milk and half the cocoa powder. Beat for about 2 minutes until the batter is pale brown and fluffy. Divide between the two pans and smooth the surfaces. Bake for about 20 minutes or until the tops of the cakes are firm and springy to the touch. Turn out the cakes onto wire racks to cool.

2   While the cakes are cooling, make the buttercream. Beat together the butter, confectioners'/icing sugar and remaining cocoa until soft and fluffy. If necessary, add 1 tsp or so of milk to get a softer consistency – you need to be able to spread this.

3   When the cakes are cold, sandwich them together with half the buttercream and spread the remaining buttercream on the top of the cake. Decorate, if you wish, with chocolate buttons or any other chocolate that takes your fancy.

Easy fruit cake

I am a bit wary of fruit cakes. The term covers those dark, dry numbers with a bit of marzipan and rock-hard frosting that lie in sad little fingers on a tray, getting drier and drier and sadder and sadder. A bad fruit cake is a depressing, soul-destroying affair. A good fruit cake is a wonderful, life-affirming experience that makes you savour the juiciness and richness – and that's even without the addition of a little alcohol. This is a recipe for a boiled fruit cake – the stuff of everyday.

²/₃ cup/4 oz/110 g raisins
²/₃ cup/4 oz/110 g ready-to-eat dried apricots
¹/₃ cup/1¾ oz/50 g dried cherries
²/₃ cup/4 oz/110 g dried peaches (or pears)
²/₃ cup/5 fl oz/150 ml water
1 stick/4 oz/110 g unsalted butter
²/₃ cup/4 oz/110 g dark muscovado sugar
2 large free-range eggs, beaten
1 tsp mixed spice
1²/₃ cups/8 oz/225 g self-rising/-raising flour, sifted

1 Preheat the oven to 300°F/150°C/ Gas mark 2. Grease and line an 8 in/20 cm cake pan/tin. Put the dried fruit, water, butter and sugar into a pan and heat gently until the mixture comes up to simmering point. Simmer for about 20 minutes, giving it a stir every now and again to stop the mixture sticking.

2 Let the mixture cool for a while – if you add the eggs while it's too hot you get scrambled eggs. When it's cool, add the eggs and spice and sift the flour over the top of it all. Mix it all up well – and this is where you really don't need a mixer; a wooden spoon is perfect.

3 Tip the batter into the pan and smooth the top. I like to make a little indent in the centre of the cake as I think it helps to prevent it doming. Bake for about 1½ hours, checking after an hour to see if it's done by sticking a knife or a skewer in to see if it comes out clean. If it needs longer in the oven and the top is getting a bit too brown, cover it in parchment paper.

4 Leave the cake to cool in the pan for about 20 minutes before turning out onto a wire rack to cool.

Carrot cake

I make this in a square pan, but there is absolutely no reason why you have to. This is a recipe that positively welcomes additions: raisins, orange zest, chopped nuts, different spices or toppings all work really well. View this as a base carrot cake recipe and make it your own – indeed, it need never be the same twice.

¾ cup/6 fl oz/175 ml sunflower oil

1 cup/6 oz/175 g soft light brown sugar

3 large free-range eggs

1 cup/5 oz/150 g all-purpose/plain flour

1½ tsp baking soda/bicarbonate of soda

1½ tsp baking powder

1 tsp ground cinnamon

2 cups/8 oz/225 g grated carrot

¼ stick/1 oz/25 g unsalted butter

1¾ cups/7 oz/200 g confectioners'/icing sugar, sifted

1¾ tbsp/1 oz/25 g cream cheese

1 Preheat the oven to 350°F/180°C/ Gas mark 4. Grease and line an 8 in/20 cm square pan/tin. In a large bowl, whisk together the oil and the brown sugar, then add the eggs and whisk away. Sift in the flour, baking soda/bicarbonate of soda, baking powder and cinnamon and whisk some more. When everything is fully whisked, stir in the grated carrot. Pour the batter into the pan and bake for 20–25 minutes until the top is springy and an inserted knife or skewer comes out clean. Leave the cake to cool in its pan for 10 minutes before turning it onto a wire rack to cool completely.

2 Meanwhile, make the icing. Cream together the butter and confectioners'/icing sugar until well incorporated and the butter has really softened. The mixture should be really quite stiff. Then carefully work in the cream cheese – don't overdo it, because it can make the topping go really runny. If it gets too thin, just add more confectioners' sugar until you obtain the consistency you are after. Add any flavouring you like at this stage: orange juice or zest, a smidge of honey, vanilla – anything that takes your fancy. Spread the frosting over the cake and enjoy.

THE FROSTING ON THE CAKE

Here are three very straightforward types of frosting that you can easily whip up to adorn your baked goodies. The first is glacé frosting made with water or lemon juice. It's a question of sieving the confectioners' sugar, adding the liquid and stirring. That's it. The second frosting is buttercream. Butter, sifted confectioners' sugar. Stir (albeit quickly in a beating-type manner). Flavours, colours and embellishments may be added, but they are a doddle.

Even simpler is spreading something on top a cake or muffin straight out of a jar or tub. Why not? Nutella, lemon curd, mascarpone, whipped heavy cream – all delicious and simply divine spread on top. I feel I should point out that low in effort doesn't actually mean low in cost. An Extremely Posh Rose Cupcake is really quite extravagant – those roses don't come cheap. Hey-ho. All worth it in the world of cupcake exquisiteness!

For cakes that involve a bit more fiddling and twiddling and where you have to make some decorations in advance, rolled fondant frosting is the order of the day. Fondant is made with powdered confectioners' sugar which generally has had some dried glycerine added to it. It's versatile, easy to handle and comes in a wide range of colours.

You will see that I am partial to a drop of colour on my cake. I remember one woman wanting reassurance that the electric-blue cake that little Crispin was about to tuck into was entirely natural. I looked at the vivid blue and looked at her and had to break it to her that, in fact, there was nothing very natural about a food item that bright. Having said that, there are companies out there who produce quite a range of tartrazine-free colours for those whose eyes start spinning and their skin forming a thin film of sweat when it comes to artificial colours – and that's just the parents waiting for their children to absorb the colour and go on a behaviour free fall.

Gels are much better than the liquid colourings. They don't thin the frosting and the colours tend to be much more versatile. I love them. You can get them from good kitchen shops and sugarcraft specialists. Word of warning: a little goes a long way.

Tasty buttercream

COFFEE
Add 1 tsp very, very, very strong espresso or filter coffee (made with instant coffee – 3 tsp coffee granules with just enough boiling water to make it liquid). Mix through thoroughly.

CHOCOLATE
Add 2 tsp sifted cocoa powder to the buttercream mixture. If you want it more chocolatey, add more. If you are feeling very extravagant, melt 2 oz/60 g good-quality bittersweet (at least 70% cocoa solids) chocolate in a bowl over a pan of simmering water, and add that, too. Mix through thoroughly.

LEMON
Add the grated zest of 1 unwaxed lemon and 2 tsp freshly squeezed lemon juice. Mix through thoroughly. This works well with lime, too. And orange, come to that.

Glacé frosting

This is the simplest and most useful frosting. Minimum ingredients and minimum fuss. Very easily correctible if you make it too thick or too thin.

Makes enough for 12 cupcakes

1¼ cups/7 oz/200 g confectioners'/icing sugar, sifted
Juice of 1 large lemon OR ¼ cup/55 ml/2 fl oz boiling water
Gel food colouring of your choice

Put the sifted confectioners'/icing sugar in a bowl. Add the liquid slowly, a little at a time, and stir until smooth. Stop adding liquid when you like the look of the consistency. It should be a smidgen thicker than heav/double cream. Add a tiny amount of colour – use a cocktail stick/toothpick dipped into the colour. You can always add more if you want, but there is no way to undo a lurid amount of colour without making a super-huge batch of icing.

Buttercream

Not for those watching their waistlines, this righ, sweet, melt-in-the-mouth frosting is equally delicious as a filling between layers of cake. Just make sure you beat it really well so it is light and fluffy.

Makes enough for 12 cupcakes

1½ cups/8 oz/225 g confectioners'/icing sugar, sifted
3½ oz/100 g soft unsalted butter
½ tsp vanilla extract (optional)

Beat everything together in a large bowl for a few minutes until light and fluffy. If the mixture looks a little on the heavy side, ½ tsp boiling water whisked in works wonders.

If you want coloured or flavoured buttercream, add away to your heart's content (see suggestions opposite).

Royal icing

This is a great frosting for decorating. It's not that tricky, but you need to watch the consistency. A frosting that hold peaks like a meringue is what you need.

Makes enough for 24 cupcakes

2 large free-range egg whites
About 3¼ cups/1 lb 2 oz/500 g confectioners'/icing sugar, sifted
2 tsp freshly squeezed lemon juice

Put everything into a large mixing bowl, and whisk away for 4–5 minutes until the mixture is very white and standing in stiff peaks. It should be really quite stiff. If the mixture is too cement-like, add a few drops of lemon juice or boiling water. If it is too runny, add a little more sifted confectioners'/icing sugar. This makes a lot of icing, so you may wish to halve the quantity, but it does keep well for around a week in the refrigerator if you seal it really well. I put a layer of plastic wrap on top of the surface, then seal in an airtight plastic container.

USING A DECORATING BAG

— ◀ ● ▶ —

Many people are put off using a decorating bag because it looks a little bit tricky. The key is to practice first on a plate or piece of paper until you get the feel for it and are able to control the flow of frosting from the tube. And once you can do that, you're well on your way to professional-looking cakes, cupcakes and cookies – and you'll be able to use your new-found skills with both buttercream and royal icing.

Decorating tubes

The tubes are the metal or plastic cone-shaped pieces that you place inside the decorating bag. The frosting is squeezed through the tube, and different types of tube give different effects. A small plain round end is best to start with, to practice simple lines and dots with royal icing. Then you can experiment with the different patterns achieved by different tube ends. For buttercream, use a star-shaped tube at first to practice swirls. These are particularly effective on cupcakes!

Decorating with royal icing

Royal icing is great for adding details to cakes, cookies and cupcakes. It is also very simple to mix with colouring pastes so can be used to add little splashes of colour to an otherwise plain treat.

Dots

The consistency of your royal icing is absolutely crucial – too stiff and your dots will be awkward-shaped peaks; too runny and your lines will disappear into the background. Experiment until you get it just right, and only then make a start on your cakes! Hold the bag comfortably in your writing hand, moving it around until you feel in control of the tube. Practice dots first on a plate or piece of card. Hold the decorating bag so the tube is just slightly above and perpendicular to the surface to be decorated. In one smooth movement, squeeze the bag so the icing pools around the tube, release the pressure on the bag and then pull the tube upwards and away from the dot. The dot should settle to form a perfect dome. If it still has a peak after a couple of minutes, your icing is too stiff.

> You can control the size of your dots by squeezing more or less icing through the tube, and can create patterns just by changing the size of the dots.

Lines

To create lines, hold the decorating bag in the same way as for dots, but angle the tip at about 45 degrees to the surface you are decorating. Touch the tip of the tube to the surface, then start squeezing the decorating bag at the same time as you start moving the tube slowly across your surface. Ensure you keep the tube moving at the same rate as the flow of icing for a smooth line – too fast and you'll break the line; too slow and you'll get uneven width. To finish a line neatly touch the tip of the tube to the surface, release the pressure on the bag and bring the nozzle up and away from the surface, much the same as piping dots.

Decorating with buttercream

Buttercream is so simple to make, and if you go the extra mile and apply it with a decorating bag you'll be rewarded with professional, beautiful results. You can then use sprinkles, sugar decorations, chocolate chips – anything edible and pretty to enhance your buttercream topping. Or you can leave it plain and let the swirls steal the show.

Swirls

Choose a tube that has a star-shaped end, and is reasonably large (about ½ in/12 mm in diameter). It's great to use a saucer to practice with, as you can use the indented circle in the centre. Rest the decorating bag tube at the outside edge of the indented circle (or if using a plate, an imaginary circle around 2½ in/6 cm in diameter). At the same time, begin steadily squeezing the bag and moving the tube around the outside of the circle. Keep squeezing and moving until you get to where you started, and then continue on the inside of the buttercream circle. You are creating a spiral, which on a flat surface will remain quite flat, but on a domed cupcake will make a wonderful conical shape. Once you reach the centre, release the pressure on the decorating bag and pull it vertically upwards to finish the swirl with a soft peak.

Ruffles

Buttercream ruffles are particularly good around the vertical sides of a tall cake, or around the outer edge of the top of a gateau. Choose a tube that has a long and narrow opening, either with or without a crimped edge. Practice first on a plate or piece of card. Place the end of the tube at about 45 degrees to the surface, long side down. Squeeze the decorating bag and gently but surely move it half an inch back, quarter inch forward, half an inch back, quarter inch forward and so on to create a ruffled effect.

Try twisting the tube and bag slightly as you work for an even swirlier swirl!

When decorating with buttercream try to keep your hands cool so it doesn't start to melt in the bag. Keep turning the bag, and put it in the refrigerator for 15 minutes if it begins to feel too warm and soft.

TEABREADS AND LOAVES
Baking in a loaf pan will make you feel like a true domestic goddess
– go on, give it a try! Extracted from Kate Shirazi's book *Cake Magic*,
these recipes are simple to make with impressive and delicious results.

Makes
10
slices

Marmalade & apricot teabread

When in need of a snack to keep him going, my Dad used to wander around the house clutching a marmalade sandwich. This teabread is dedicated to him. If he were still here, he'd probably enjoy it, but I do acknowledge that he'd secretly be hankering after the white bread and thick-cut Chivers approach.

Scant 1½ cups/7 oz/200 g all-purpose/
plain flour
2 tsp ground ginger
1 tsp baking powder
Scant ½ stick/1¾ oz/50 g unsalted butter
¼ cup/1¾ oz/50 g light muscovado sugar
Scant ⅔ cup/3½ oz/100 g ready-to-eat
dried apricots, chopped
4 tbsp marmalade
Scant ⅓ cup/2½ fl oz/75 ml milk
1 large free-range egg, beaten

1 Preheat the oven to 325°F/160°C/ Gas mark 3. Grease and line a 1 lb/450 g loaf pan/tin. Sift the flour, ginger and baking powder into a large bowl and rub in the butter until the mixture looks like breadcrumbs. Then stir in the sugar and the chopped apricots. In another bowl, or a jug, mix up the marmalade, milk and egg and pour that onto the dry mixture. Mix it all up really well and pour it into the pan. Level the top and bake for about 1 hour, or until golden, firm to the touch and a skewer comes out cleanly. Turn the loaf onto a wire rack to cool.

2 I sometimes make some candied orange peel to go on top, but this is entirely optional. If you want to, all you need to do is pare some strips of orange peel and put them into a pan with about ⅔ cup/5 fl oz/ 150 ml water and 3 tbsp superfine/ caster sugar. Bring the pan to the boil and then slowly simmer for about an hour or until the peel has gone translucent and the liquid has reduced by about half. Don't let the liquid reduce to a caramel or you will end up with something else altogether! Remove the orange strips from the pan and leave on silicone paper to cool and dry. Sprinkle with more superfine sugar if you wish.

Gently spiced fruit loaf

Makes a large loaf that will serve 8 peckish people

This is the sort of fruity bread that makes people whimper slightly. It has everything: warm spices, gorgeous fruit, soft bread and a drizzle of lemony icing. Ooooh. Yes, please. You decide what fruit to use – it's all good.

FOR THE DOUGH:
2¾ tbsp/1½ oz/40 g unsalted butter

2 cups/10 oz/280 g strong white bread flour

Scant ¼ cup/1¾ oz/50 g superfine/caster sugar

A pinch of salt

¼ oz/7 g sachet dried yeast

Scant ½ cup/3½ fl oz/100 ml hand-hot milk

3 large free-range egg yolks

FOR THE FILLING:
2 cups/17 fl oz/500 ml water

2 cups/1 lb/450 g dried fruit (apricots, cranberries, dates, figs, peaches, etc.), chopped

Zest and juice of 1 large unwaxed lemon

Zest and juice of 1 large orange

2 tbsp runny honey

1 tsp ground coriander

1 tsp cardamom seeds, crushed

FOR THE ICING:
Scant ¾ cup/2¾ oz/75 g confectioners'/icing sugar, sifted

Juice of 1 large lemon

Slivered/flaked almonds to sprinkle (optional)

1 Start by making the dough. In a large bowl, rub the butter into the flour until it resembles breadcrumbs and then stir in the sugar, salt and yeast. Pour in the hot milk and 2 egg yolks and mix to form a dough. Turn the dough out onto a floured surface and knead the dough until it's smooth and elastic – this will take at least 10 minutes. Put the dough back into the bowl and cover with a tea towel or a layer of plastic wrap and leave to rise somewhere warm for at least 1 hour. The dough should double in size.

2 While the dough is rising, crack on with the filling. Put the water in a big pan and bring it to the boil. Add the chopped dried fruit and simmer, stirring every now and again until the fruit is really soft. Add the citrus zest and juice, honey and spices and continue bubbling gently until the liquid has been absorbed by the fruit. Stir it every so often as it can catch on the bottom of the pan if left alone too long. Leave the mixture to cool down.

3 When the dough has doubled in size and the fruity filling is cool, take the dough out of the bowl and give it 2–3 bashes to knock the air out of it. Knead it again for another 3–4 minutes, then roll it out into a large rectangle about ½ in/1 cm thick. Spread the fruit over the surface, leaving a gap around the edge of about ¾ in/2 cm. Roll up the dough as you would a Swiss/jelly roll and press the edges together to seal, then coil it around so you end up with a circular sausage. Place it on a baking sheet with the seal underneath. Pop the tea towel over the top again and leave it in the warm place for another hour to rise.

4 Preheat the oven to 180°C/350°F/Gas mark 4 and, just before the loaf goes in the oven, brush it all over with the remaining egg yolk. Bake for about 20 minutes. It will be done when it is risen and golden on the top and the bottom sounds hollow when you give it a knock. Cool the loaf on a wire rack and make a very thin icing with the confectioners'/icing sugar and lemon juice. When cool, randomly drizzle the icing over the top of the loaf and sprinkle the almonds on top, if liked.

Apple & walnut teabread

This teabread has to be one of the most versatile numbers going. Make it sweet, make it savoury, make it big, make it small – it really is a wonder. Just delicious with a lump of strong Cheddar, or equally good with a smear of butter and a cup of tea – even au naturel, shoved in a lunch box. It's easy to make and keeps well for ages in an airtight container. Surely this recipe must belong to a 'hero' category?

Scant 1 stick/3½ oz/100 g unsalted butter
Scant ½ cup/3½ oz/100 g superfine/
caster sugar
2 large free-range eggs
1 tbsp corn/golden syrup
⅔ cup/3½ oz/100 g golden raisins/sultanas
¾ cup/3½ oz/100 g chopped walnuts
1⅔ cups/8 oz/225 g self-rising/
-raising flour
1 tsp mixed spice
1 tsp ground cinnamon
2 dessert apples, peeled, cored and
chopped (I use Braeburn or Cox's)

1   Preheat the oven to 325°F/160°C/ Gas mark 3. Grease and line a 1½ lb/680 g loaf pan/tin or lay out 12 mini loaf cases on a baking sheet. Put all the ingredients into a big bowl and give them a bit of a beating. I put them in the mixer because I'm lazy, but a wooden spoon would be just as good. Don't use a food processor, though, because you will pulverize the apple too much.

2   Tip the lot into the loaf pan or mini loaf cases and bake the biggie for about 1 hour or the littlies for about 20 minutes. A knife or skewer will come out cleanly when they are cooked. Cool the big one on a wire rack and leave the little ones to cool in their cases.

Cheddar & rosemary bread

This lovely loaf can be made freeform to have hunks torn off for lunch or baked in a loaf pan for thin slices, buttered and quartered and presented nicely on a plate for afternoon tea. The herb doesn't have to be rosemary – thyme would also be great – and the cheese doesn't have to be Cheddar. Any hard cheese with plenty of flavour would be fine.

3½ cups/1 lb 2 oz/500 g strong white bread flour

1 tsp salt

1 tsp superfine/caster sugar

3 tsp English mustard powder

⅓ oz/10 g dried yeast

1¼ cups/10 fl oz/300 ml tepid water

2 tsp fresh rosemary, chopped

10 ½ cups/10 oz/300 g grated strong Cheddar cheese

1   In a large bowl, stir together the flour, salt, sugar, mustard powder and yeast, then add the water and mix until a dough forms. Tip the dough onto a well-floured work surface and get kneading like you mean it for at least 10 minutes, but maybe 15. You may stop when the dough is smooth and elastic and doesn't feel straggly under your fingers. Form the dough into a ball and score a large, deep cross in the top. Put it back in the bowl, cover with a tea towel and leave somewhere warm to rise – this will probably take about 1 hour.

2   When the dough has doubled in size, bash it about to knock out all the air and start kneading again, this time adding 1²/₃ cups/ 7 oz/200 g grated cheese in three goes. Just sprinkle a third over the dough and start kneading; when it has been incorporated, add the next third and so on. When all the cheese is in, knead the dough for another 5 minutes before either forming it into a loose shape and placing on a baking sheet, or putting it into a greased and floured 21/4 lb/1 kg pan/tin. Make lots of dimpled holes in the top of the loaf with your fingers, sprinkle the mustard powder and remaining cheese over the top and prod in a bit more. Cover the dough again with the tea towel and leave once more in the warm place to rise for another hour.

3   Preheat the oven to 375°F/190°C/ Gas mark 5. The baking time depends on what shape you have made, but it should be around the 20-minute mark. You will know when it is done by tapping the bottom of the loaf. If it sounds hollow, it is ready. If you have cooked it in a pan, turn out onto a wire rack to cool.

SUMMER PARTY MENUS

Have fun in the sun with these delicious party menus – whether you need baked treats that are easy to pack up and take on a picnic, or are entertaining at home in the summer.

Perfect Picnic

Cheddar & Rosemary Bread **58**

86 Smoked Salmon Muffins

Carrot Cupcakes **22**

18 Choc chip shortbread

Pack these baked goodies up with cold drinks, fresh salads, cheeses and cold meats for a delicious summer day out.

Elegant Garden Party

Coffee Cake **40**

---

96 Raspberry & White Chocolate Cake

Battenburg Cupcakes **26**

---

12 Lemon Cookies

*Supply guests with coloured napkins
in pretty summer colours to help
catch those cake crumbs!*

GO TO THE PAGES LISTED FOR FULL RECIPES AND INSTRUCTIONS

KNEAD IT!

Nothing compares to the scent of homemade bread baking in the oven. Morning, noon or night, it'll cheer up your home and induce healthy appetites for everyone within its walls!

The most commonly used flour for breadmaking is wheat. Strong wheat flour has a high gluten content and gives a better volume of bread, as it absorbs more water and makes a lighter dough.

White flour is made from the starchy part of the grain from which the fibre and wheatgerm has been removed. Whole-wheat flour is made from 100 per cent of the grain; nothing is added and nothing is taken away. Wheatmeal is made from 81–85 per cent of the grain and some of the fibre and wheatgerm has been removed.

Bread can be made with various other grains. Rye gives a dark dough and is usually mixed half and half with wheat flour; barley gives a cake-like texture and is usually mixed with wheat flour; maize gives a crumbly, crunchy texture. Other ingredients can be added to achieve different results: for example, extra bran, wheatgerm, sesame, poppy or sunflower seeds, cheese, herbs, spices, lemon or orange rind and rye flakes.

Kneading

Kneading is an essential part of breadmaking as it helps to develop the gluten and the rise of the dough. Flour a board and use the palms of the hands, almost to the wrists, to push and turn the dough. As you work you can actually feel the texture changing to a smooth, elastic but not sticky consistency.

Don't underestimate the amount of time and energy that's needed to turn your dough from initial mix to perfectly smooth and elastic bread dough. It's a fantastic work out for your arms, so get some music on and pump those fists! Had a hard day at work? Kids driving you nuts? Breadmaking is particularly good therapy for getting rid of all those frustrations.

Fresh or dried yeast?

Dried or instant yeast can be substituted for fresh yeast. For ½ oz/15 g fresh yeast use ¼ oz/6.25 g dried or instant yeast, for 1 oz/25 g fresh yeast use ½ oz/10.5 g dried or instant yeast and for 2 oz/50 g fresh yeast use ¾ oz/21 g dried or instant yeast. If using dried yeast, dissolve in a little liquid of the recipe before adding to the other ingredients. If using instant yeast, add to the dry ingredients before mixing in the other ingredients. If using dried or instant yeast, the dough only needs to rise once.

Rising

Always cover the dough when setting it to rise; any draughts may affect the rising process, and even without draughts you don't want the surface of your dough to dry out. The yeast in the dough needs warmth to start working; the ideal temperature is between 98 and 110°F/36 and 44°C. Too much heat will kill the yeast; too little will stop it from working. The best place to leave dough to rise is on top of an Aga, a boiler or an active tumble dryer. The time taken for the dough to rise will depend on the warmth, but it usually takes 1–1½ hours. The second rising is quicker, usually between 20 minutes and half an hour.

Troubleshooting

If the loaf is smaller than expected, the yeast probably did not activate properly due to incorrect temperature during rising. If the texture is coarse, the yeast was not properly mixed at the beginning, or there was too much yeast, which caused excessive rising and air in the dough.

Many freestanding mixers come with a dough hook. This can save you a lot of toil – just follow the manufacturrer's instructions for the best results.

See pages 104–105 for more about the different flours used in baking.

BEAUTIFUL BREAD

There is nothing quite like the taste of a handmade, homemade loaf of bread fresh out of the oven. Breakfast, brunch, lunch or dinner, fresh bread is always a welcome addition to the table!

BASIC WHITE BREAD

Makes 1 loaf

This is easy to make, does not require a bread machine, and gives the home baker a base from which to experiment.

3²/₃ cups/1 lb 2 oz/500 g strong white bread flour
A large pinch of sea salt
½ oz/15 g instant/active dry or fresh yeast
Scant 1 cup/7 fl oz/200 ml warm water
1 medium egg
Scant ½ cup/3½ fl oz/100 ml milk

Place the flour in a large bowl, add the salt and mix well.

If using instant yeast, pour it over the flour (if using fresh yeast, whisk it into the warm water; make sure the water is the temperature of a tepid bath, if it is any hotter you will kill the yeast). Make a well in the middle of the flour and, using a wooden spoon, add the warm (see above) water (or warm water and fresh yeast), mixing until you have a slightly soggy-looking paste. Tip this paste onto a well-floured surface, then knead for 10–15 minutes, adding flour if necessary, until the dough becomes firm and elastic and ceases to stick to the work surface.

Put the dough into a floured mixing bowl, cover with a clean damp cloth and put it in a warm place such as an airing cupboard for 1 hour.

Remove the dough from the mixing bowl and place it on a floured work surface. Form it into a sausage shape and put it into a non-stick baking pan/tin. The dough should come two-thirds of the way up the inside of the pan.

Beat the egg and milk together, then paint the top of the dough with this eggwash. Allow to rise for 30–40 minutes until the dough comes above the top of the baking pan/tin.

Preheat the oven to 425°F/220°C/Gas mark 7. Brush the top of the dough again lightly with the eggwash and bake on a baking sheet for 10 minutes, then turn the oven down to 350°F/180°C/Gas mark 4 and bake for a further 20 minutes.

Tip the bread out and check that the sides and bottom of the loaf are fully baked. Leave to cool on a wire rack for 1 hour before cutting.

Historically, white bread was purely for the wealthy and was a status symbol, which today we take for granted. The bread that the peasants ate would have been coarse whole-wheat, containing large amounts of husk and impurities.

For more delicious bread recipes, pick up a copy of *Countrywise Country Cook Book* by Mike Robinson.

Brewery bread with crystal malt

By making bread, using beer as both the liquid and the raising agent, you are creating something with a unique flavour. One of the most important ingredients in the production of British real ale is malted barley. Different strengths of malted barley produce different flavoured and coloured beers, and my favourite is golden crystal malt. Dave Maggs, who owns the West Berkshire Brewery uses locally produced crystal malt to make several of his beers. I love to sprinkle that delicious, crunchy malt over this bread just before it goes into the oven. The results are fantastic.

Makes 1 loaf

1½ cups/9 oz/250 g strong whole-wheat/wholemeal flour
1²/₃ cups/9 oz/250 g strong white bread flour
A handful of crystal malt
1 tbsp salt
¾ oz/20 g instant/active dry yeast
2½ tbsp/1¼ oz/30 g butter, melted
1¼ cups/10 fl oz/300 ml good local beer
1 egg for eggwash
Onion seeds
Sea salt

Mix all the dry ingredients except the onion seeds and salt together in a large bowl, then make a well in the centre and pour in the melted butter and beer. Stir to form a dough.

Tip the dough out onto a lightly floured work surface and knead for 10 minutes, then put it back into the bowl and leave it to rest in a warm place for 1 hour.

Return the dough to the floured work surface and shape it into a ball, then flatten it and roll it up. Put the dough on a greased baking sheet and leave it to rise for a further hour.

Preheat the oven to 400°F/200°C/Gas mark 6. Beat the egg. Cut several slashes across the top of the bread and glaze with the egg. Sprinkle liberally with onion seeds and sea salt. Bake for 30 minutes, then transfer to a wire rack to cool.

Irish soda bread

Soda bread is unique. Traditionally a poor-man's bread from Ireland, it has now attained something akin to cult status. Nothing quite compares to the nutty aroma of baking or cooling soda bread. It has great advantages for the modern cook over normal types of bread, in that it requires no rising. The basic principle, of course, is that it uses baking soda and buttermilk in place of yeast. The most important thing to remember when making it is to do as little kneading as possible; the looser the dough, the better. Traditionally, the cross-shaped cut on top of the soda bread was made to bless the bread and the corners were pricked to allow the fairies to escape.

Makes 1 loaf

3¼ cups/1 lb/450 g strong white bread flour (to make brown soda bread, use half whole-wheat/wholemeal flour and half white bread flour)
1 tsp salt
1 tsp baking soda/bicarbonate of soda
1½–1¾ cups/12–14 fl oz/350–400 ml sour milk or buttermilk, to mix

Preheat the oven to 450°F/230°C/Gas mark 8.

Sift the dry ingredients into a bowl. Make a well in the centre. Pour most of the milk in, then using one hand, mix in the flour from the sides of the bowl, adding more milk if necessary. The dough should be softish, not too wet and sticky.

When it all comes together, turn it out on to a well-floured work surface, then pat the dough into a circle about 1½ in/4 cm thick. Put a cross on it and prick the corners. Put on a baking sheet.

Bake for 15 minutes, then turn the oven down to 400°F/200°C/gas mark 6 and bake for a further 30 minutes or until cooked. If you are in doubt, tap the bottom of the bread – if it is cooked, it will sound hollow. Cool on a wire rack.

Buttermilk oaten bread

Fine oatmeal gives a wonderful gritty texture to this favourite Irish bread. Buttermilk was once a staple ingredient in breads and cakes, and gave a slightly sour taste and good keeping qualities. Serve this as a satisfying part of 'high tea', warm with cheese or toasted with melting butter and thick fruity jams.

Generous 1 cup/7 oz/200 g fine oatmeal
1¼ cups/10 fl oz/300 ml buttermilk
½ cup/4 fl oz/120 ml milk
1¾ cups/9 oz/250 g all-purpose/plain flour, sifted
1 tsp baking powder
¼ tsp salt

Soak the oatmeal in the buttermilk and milk overnight. The following day preheat the oven to 350°F/180°C/Gas mark 4. Grease a baking sheet. Mix together the flour, baking powder and salt. Add the oatmeal and milk mixture and mix well to give a soft dough. Knead until smooth. Divide into two portions and, on a floured board, roll each portion out to a thickness of about 1 in/2.5 cm and about 4 in/10 cm in diameter. Place both loaves on the prepared sheet and bake for 35–40 minutes until they are golden and sound hollow when tapped. Remove from the oven and serve hot with butter.

Makes
2 small
loaves

Sesame rolls

From Trerice in Cornwall, these little rolls enjoy the sweet nuttiness of sesame and are delicious at teatime filled with smoked salmon or honey roast ham. The glory of Trerice is the south-facing drawing room – a perfect room in which to take tea. Displayed here are some fine examples of Chinese porcelain tea bowls and little pots that were imported on the same ships that brought the chests of tea from the Orient. European potters were amazed at the fine, translucent quality of the Chinese wares when they first came across them in the middle of the 17th century and spent the following fifty years or so attempting to manufacture something equally beautiful.

Makes 14

½ oz/15 g fresh yeast (to substitute dried yeast, see page 62)
2 tsp superfine/caster sugar
1¾ cups/14 fl oz/400 ml water, warmed
4¾ cups/1½ lb/675 g strong white bread flour, sifted
1½ tsp full-cream milk powder (Coffeemate or similar)
½ tsp salt
¼ stick/1 oz/25 g butter, softened
1 egg, beaten and mixed with a little water
2–3 tbsp sesame seeds

Mix together the yeast, sugar and 6 tbsp/3 fl oz/75 ml of the water. Leave in a warm place for about 20–30 minutes until frothy. Mix together the flour, milk powder and salt and rub in the fat. Add the yeast mixture and the remaining water and mix to a pliable dough. Knead until smooth and elastic, then place in a bowl, cover with a damp cloth and leave in a warm place for 1–1½ hours until doubled in size. Grease two baking sheets. When the dough is well risen, divide into 2½ oz/65 g pieces, form these into bun shapes and place on the prepared sheets. Brush the tops with eggwash and sprinkle liberally with sesame seeds. Leave in a warm place for about 30 minutes until well risen. Meanwhile, preheat the oven to 400°F/200°C/Gas mark 6. When the rolls are well risen, bake for 20–25 minutes until golden brown and firm. Remove from the oven and lift onto a wire rack to cool. Serve warm or cold. If liked stir 1 tbsp of sesame seeds into the dough with the yeast mixture. Sprinkle as above with more seeds before baking.

Boxty bread

Boxty bread is traditional festive Irish bread, flat and round and marked into four portions before baking to allow for easy division once cooked. With potatoes its essentially Irish ingredient, it was once an indulgence for Shrove Tuesday, All Saints' Day or Halloween.

Makes 2 small round flat loaves

8 oz/225 g raw potatoes
8 oz/225 g mashed potatoes
1²/₃ cups/8 oz/225 g all-purpose/plain flour, sifted
¼ cup/2 oz/50 g butter, melted
Salt and freshly ground black pepper

Preheat the oven to 375°F/190°C/Gas mark 5. Grease a baking sheet. Wash and peel the raw potatoes. Grate into a clean cloth and wring well over a bowl to squeeze out the juice. Place the grated potatoes in a bowl with the mashed potatoes and mix well together. Leave the starchy liquid in the bowl until the starch has settled, then pour off the liquid and add the starch to the potatoes. Add the flour, melted butter and seasoning and mix to a soft dough. Knead well. Divide into two portions and, on a floured board, roll into flat circles. Place on the baking sheet and divide the top of each loaf into four with a sharp knife. Bake for 40 minutes until firm and golden. Remove from the oven and serve hot with plenty of butter.

For more delicious traditional British bread recipes, pick up a copy of *Good Old-fashioned Teatime Baking* from The National Trust.

Organic whole-wheat bread

This lovely nutty-flavoured bread comes from Branscombe Bakery, the last traditional bakery to be used in Devon. Until 1987 it was run by brothers Gerald and Stuart Collier who baked bread, buns, cakes, tarts and scones every day of the year. The oven was lit at four o'clock every morning and then, three hours later when it had reached the required temperature, the ashes were raked out, the oven cleaned and then the first batch of 130 loaves arranged inside.

Makes 2 x 2 lb/900 g loaves

1 oz/25 g fresh yeast (to substitute dried yeast, see page 62)
½ tsp light or dark soft brown sugar
2½–3 cups/20–24 fl oz/600–750 ml warm water (it should be almost hand-hot, and the amount needed varies according to the flour used)
6½ cups/2 lb/900 g organic whole-wheat/wholemeal flour, sifted and warmed slightly in the oven
1 tbsp sea salt
1 tbsp corn or sunflower oil
1 tbsp clear honey

Cream together the yeast and sugar and blend with 4–6 tbsp/2–3 fl oz/50–75ml of the warm water. Leave in a warm, draught-free place for 10–20 minutes until frothy – there should be at least ¾ in/1.5 cm of froth on the top. Mix together the flour and salt and make a well in the middle. Pour in the oil, honey, yeast mixture and enough of the remaining water to give a soft, elastic dough. Knead with the hands for about 10 minutes. Shape the dough into a ball and place in a lightly greased bowl. Dust the top with a little flour, cover with a clean damp cloth and leave in a warm, draught-free place until almost doubled in size (this can take anything from 50 minutes to 2 hours). Grease two 2 lb/900 g loaf pans/tins. Turn the dough out onto a lightly floured board and knead vigorously for 8–10 minutes. Divide the dough into two equal portions and shape to fit the pans. Place in the pans, sprinkle the tops with a little more flour and cover with a clean damp cloth. Leave in a warm place for a further 30–40 minutes until the dough reaches the top of the pans. Meanwhile, preheat the oven to 425°F/220°C/Gas mark 7. When the dough has risen, bake the loaves for 30 minutes. Remove from the oven and remove from the pans. Place the loaves in the oven for a further 10–15 minutes until they sound hollow when tapped. Remove from the oven and cool on a wire rack.

SWEET AND SAVOURY MUFFINS

Muffins are a vehicle for almost endless flavour combinations, both sweet and savoury. And they couldn't be easier to make! These mouthwatering recipes are from Susannah Blake's *Muffin Magic* book, where you can find even more delicious flavour combinations to try.

Apple muffins with cinnamon butter

Makes 12

Throw together a batch of these comforting muffins and find your kitchen filled with the sweet smell of cinnamon. For a fuss-free but to-die-for twist, serve them still warm, broken open and smeared with melting cinnamon butter.

2 cups/10 oz/300 g self-rising/-raising flour
½ tsp baking soda/bicarbonate of soda
1 tsp ground cinnamon
2 eggs, beaten
Scant ⅓ cup/3 fl oz/85 ml plain yogurt
Scant ½ cup/3½ fl oz/100 ml milk
⅔ cup/4 oz/110 g soft brown sugar
6 tbsp sunflower oil
2 apples, peeled, cored and finely diced

FOR THE CINNAMON BUTTER
1 stick/4 oz/110 g butter, at room temperature
½ cup/2 oz/60 g confectioners'/icing sugar, sifted
1 tsp ground cinnamon

1   Preheat the oven to 400°F/200°C/ Gas mark 6. Grease or line a 12-hole muffin pan/tin.

2   Combine the flour, baking soda/ bicarbonate of soda and cinnamon and sift into a large bowl.

3   In a separate bowl, combine the eggs, yogurt, milk, brown sugar and oil, then stir in the apples. Pour the mixture into the dry ingredients and stir together until just combined, then spoon big dollops of the batter into the prepared muffin pan.

4   Bake for about 20 minutes until risen and golden. Leave to cool in the pan for a couple of minutes, then transfer to a wire rack to cool.

5   Meanwhile, beat together the butter, confectioners'/icing sugar and cinnamon. Serve the muffins warm, with the cinnamon butter for spreading.

Makes
12

Lemon & almond crumbles

Lemony, almondy, moist, moreish ... what's not to like? These are another of those easy-peasy muffins that somehow elicit an air of sophistication and make you feel rather ladylike — until you find yourself trying to resist the urge to eat more than one!

1²/₃ cups/8 oz/225 g self-rising/
-raising flour
1 tsp baking powder
Scant ²/₃ cup/5 oz/150 g superfine/
caster sugar
Generous 1 cup/4 oz/110 g ground
almonds
1 egg, beaten
1 cup/8 fl oz/225 ml milk
Scant ½ cup/3 oz/85 g butter, melted
grated zest of 2 lemons
½ cup/1½ oz/40 g slivered/flaked almonds
for sprinkling
Confectioners'/icing sugar for dusting

1 Preheat the oven to 400°F/200°C/
Gas mark 6. Grease or line a 12-
hole muffin pan/tin.

2 Combine the flour, baking powder
and superfine/caster sugar and
sift into a large bowl. Sprinkle the
ground almonds into the bowl.

3 In a separate bowl or jug, combine
the egg, milk, butter and lemon zest,
then pour into the dry ingredients.
Stir together until just combined,
then spoon big dollops of the batter
into the prepared muffin pan.
Sprinkle the tops with the
slivered/flaked almonds.

4 Bake for about 20 minutes until
risen and golden. Leave to cool in
the pan for a few minutes, then
transfer to a wire rack to cool.
Serve dusted with confectioners'/
icing sugar.

Espresso express

Make these in the morning when you need a bit of jet-fuel to get you going. After munching your way through the coffee-flavoured crumb specked with whole chocolate-covered coffee beans and all topped off with a lusciously creamy, sugary coffee buttercream, nothing's going to stop you!

2 cups/10 oz/300 g all-purpose/plain flour
1 tbsp baking powder
Scant ⅔ cup/5 oz/150 g superfine/
caster sugar
¼ cup/1½ oz/40 g chocolate-covered
coffee beans
1 egg, beaten
¾ cup/6 fl oz/175 ml milk
2 tbsp Greek yogurt
2 tbsp instant coffee, dissolved in 2 tbsp
boiling water
¾ stick/3 oz/85 g butter, melted

FOR THE TOPPING
Scant 1 stick/3½ oz/100 g butter, at
room temperature
1¾ cups/7 oz/200 g confectioners'/icing
sugar, sifted
2 tsp instant coffee, dissolved in 1 tbsp
boiling water
Chocolate-covered coffee beans
to decorate

1   Preheat the oven to 400°F/200°C/ Gas mark 6. Grease or line a 12-hole muffin pan/tin.

2   Combine the flour, baking powder and superfine/caster sugar and sift into a large bowl, then scatter the coffee beans on top.

3   In a separate bowl or jug, lightly beat together the egg, milk, yogurt and coffee, then stir in the melted butter. Pour into the dry ingredients and stir together until just combined, then spoon big dollops of the batter into the prepared muffin pan.

4   Bake for about 20 minutes until risen and firm to the touch. Leave to cool in the pan for a few minutes, then transfer the muffins to a wire rack to cool completely.

5   To decorate, beat together the butter, confectioners'/icing sugar and coffee until smooth and creamy. Swirl on top of the muffins and decorate with more chocolate-covered coffee beans.

Peppermint stick muffins

Let the kids help you make these magnificently minty muffins. They'll love bashing the mints to break them up, and save you a lot of energy! Look out for stripy sticks of rock or candy cane and tint the frosting in a contrasting colour to really make them stand out.

Makes 12

2 cups/10 oz/300 g self-rising/-raising flour
1 tsp baking powder
Generous ⅓ cup/3 oz/85 g superfine/caster sugar
2 packets of extra strong mints (1½ oz/40 g each)
2 eggs, beaten
1 cup/8 fl oz/225 ml milk
Scant ½ cup/3 oz/85 g butter, melted

TO DECORATE
3 sticks of peppermint candy cane or rock (about 3 oz/85 g)
1¾ cups/7 oz/200 g confectioners'/icing sugar, sifted
2 tbsp lemon juice
Food colouring (optional)

1 Preheat the oven to 400°F/200°C/Gas mark 6. Grease or line a 12-hole muffin pan/tin.

2 Combine the flour, baking powder and superfine/caster sugar, then sift into a bowl. Put the mints in a mortar and pound with a pestle to break them up into small pieces. Scatter them over the flour.

3 In a separate bowl or jug, lightly beat together the eggs and milk to combine, then stir in the butter. Pour into the dry ingredients and stir together until just combined, then spoon dollops of the batter into the prepared muffin pan.

4 Bake for about 20 minutes until risen and golden. Leave to cool in the pan for a few minutes, then transfer to a wire rack to cool.

5 To decorate, put the candy cane or rock in a plastic bag and tap with a rolling pin to break into pieces. Set aside. Stir together the confectioners'/icing sugar and lemon juice until smooth, then add a few drops of food colouring to tint the frosting, if you like. Spoon on top of the muffins and sprinkle pieces of candy cane or rock on top.

Makes
12

Rocky roadsters

Although the rocky road combination of nuts, marshmallows and chocolate usually goes into ice cream, there's no reason why you shouldn't throw the trio into a muffin instead. If you do, you'll find yourself with an irresistible batch of the squishiest, meltiest, chunkiest muffins you've ever seen.

2 cups/10 oz/300 g self-rising/-raising flour
1 tsp baking powder
3 tbsp cocoa powder
2¾ oz/75 g milk chocolate, chopped
½ cup/2 oz/60 g walnut pieces
2 oz/60 g mini marshmallows (or large marshmallows snipped into pieces)
⅔ cup/5 oz/150 g soft brown sugar
Generous ¾ cup/7 fl oz/200 ml milk
2 eggs, beaten
Scant ½ cup/2¾ oz/75 g butter, melted

1 Preheat the oven to 400°F/200°C/ Gas mark 6. Grease or line a 12-hole muffin pan/tin.

2 Combine the flour, baking powder and cocoa and sift into a large bowl. Reserve about one-third of the chocolate chunks and nuts, then add the rest, along with the marshmallows, to the flour.

3 In a separate bowl or jug, combine the sugar, milk, eggs and butter, then pour into the dry ingredients. Stir together until just combined, then spoon big dollops of the batter into the prepared muffin pan. Gently press the reserved chocolate and nuts at random into the muffins.

4 Bake for about 20 minutes until risen and firm to the touch. Leave to cool in the pan for a few minutes, then transfer to a wire rack to cool.

Four-seed pesto sensations

Makes 12

Scented with herby pesto and heaving with seeds, these yummy, wholesome-looking muffins are jam-packed with healthy oils to keep you fighting fit and bouncing bright. Serve them as an accompaniment to a meal, or pop one in your lunchbox.

2 cups/10 oz/300 g all-purpose/plain flour
1 tbsp baking powder
1 tbsp superfine/caster sugar
½ tsp salt
2 tbsp sesame seeds
2 tbsp sunflower seeds
2 tbsp pumpkin seeds
2 tbsp poppy seeds
2 eggs, beaten
4 tbsp olive oil
3 tbsp pesto
¾ cup/6 fl oz/175 ml milk
Ground black pepper

FOR THE TOPPING
2 tsp sesame seeds
2 tsp sunflower seeds
2 tsp pumpkin seeds
2 tsp poppy seeds

1 Preheat the oven to 400°F/200°C/ Gas mark 6. Grease or line a 12-hole muffin pan/tin.

2 Combine the seeds for the topping in a bowl and set aside.

3 Combine the flour, baking powder, sugar and salt and sift into a large bowl, then sprinkle the seeds over the top.

4 In a separate bowl or jug, lightly beat together the eggs, olive oil, pesto and milk and add a good grinding of black pepper. Pour into the dry ingredients and stir together until just combined. Spoon large dollops of the batter into the prepared muffin pan, then sprinkle with the reserved topping seeds.

5 Bake for about 20 minutes until risen and golden. Leave to cool in the pan for a few minutes, then transfer the muffins to a wire rack to cool completely.

Sun-dried tomato & oregano muffins

Serve these yummy muffins warm or cold topped with sprigs of fresh oregano, and lose yourself in those rich Mediterranean flavours. For extra indulgence, split open a warm muffin and spread with herby cream cheese.

2 cups/10 oz/300 g all-purpose/plain flour
1 tbsp baking powder
½ tsp salt
3 tbsp freshly grated Parmesan,
plus extra for sprinkling
1 egg, beaten
Generous 1 cup/9 fl oz/250 ml milk
6 tbsp olive oil
6 sun-dried tomatoes, roughly chopped,
plus 1 extra for sprinkling
1 garlic clove, finely chopped
1 tsp fresh oregano
Ground black pepper

1   Preheat the oven to 375°F/190°C/ Gas mark 5. Grease or line a 12-hole muffin pan/tin.

2   Combine the flour, baking powder and salt and sift into a large bowl, then sprinkle the Parmesan into the bowl.

3   In a separate bowl, lightly beat together the egg, milk and oil to combine, then stir in the tomatoes, garlic and oregano. Add a good grinding of black pepper, then pour into the dry ingredients and stir until just combined. Spoon big dollops of the batter into the prepared muffin pan and sprinkle Parmesan and a few pieces of sun-dried tomato over each one, then grind over more black pepper.

4   Bake for about 20 minutes until well risen and golden. Leave to cool in the pan for a couple of minutes, then transfer the muffins to a wire rack to cool completely.

Makes
12

Roast pepper & black olive muffins

Add a splash of Mediterranean colour to your muffin repertoire with these gorgeous cornmeal muffins. Chunks of sweet juicy pepper, shiny black olives and the bite of black pepper make these utterly moreish. They're fuss-free, too, if you use bottled roasted peppers – although if you want to roast your own, why not?

Generous 1⅓ cups/7 oz/200 g all-purpose/plain flour
⅔ cup/3½ oz/100 g cornmeal
1 tbsp baking powder
1 tbsp superfine/caster sugar
½ tsp salt
¾ cup/6 fl oz/175 ml buttermilk
2 eggs, beaten
Scant ½ cup/3 oz/85 g butter, melted
4 large pieces of bottled roasted pepper, chopped (about 4½ oz/125 g)
½ cup/2 oz/60 g pitted black olives, halved
Ground black pepper

1 Preheat the oven to 400°F/200°C/ Gas mark 6. Grease or line a 12-hole muffin pan/tin.

2 Combine the flour, cornmeal, baking powder, sugar and salt and sift into a large bowl.

3 In a separate bowl, combine the buttermilk, eggs and butter with about two-thirds of the roasted peppers and olives, and add a good grinding of black pepper. Pour into the dry ingredients and stir together until just combined, then spoon big dollops of the batter into the prepared muffin pan. Press the remaining roasted peppers and olives into the tops of the muffins and grind over more black pepper.

4 Bake for about 20 minutes until risen and golden. Leave to cool in the pan for a few minutes, then transfer to a wire rack to cool.

Chili cornmeal muffins

These are the muffins to serve to your dairy-intolerant friends and family for breakfast, lunch or dinner. With a tender yellow crumb and sweet-spicy bite, they've got a taste of southern-style cornbread about them.

½ cup/4 oz/110 g cornmeal
1¼ cups/6 oz/175 g all-purpose/plain flour
1 tbsp baking powder
½ tsp salt
½ tsp crushed dried chilli, plus extra for sprinkling
1 egg, beaten
3 tbsp olive oil
¾ cup/6 fl oz/175 ml soya milk
½ green pepper, diced

1 Preheat the oven to 400°F/200°C/Gas mark 6. Grease or line a 12-hole muffin pan/tin.

2 Combine the cornmeal, flour, baking powder and salt and sift into a large bowl. Sprinkle over the crushed chilli.

3 In a separate bowl, combine the egg, oil and soya milk, then stir in the diced pepper. Pour into the dry ingredients and stir together, then spoon big dollops of the batter into the prepared muffin pan. Sprinkle over a little more dried chilli.

4 Bake for about 15 minutes until risen and firm. Leave to cool in the pan for a few minutes, then transfer to a wire rack to cool.

Makes
12

Smoked salmon muffins

In all honesty, muffins probably aren't the most sophisticated baked treat known to mankind. But these ones made with smoked salmon and cream cheese are doing their level best to try! Try serving them as a quirky savoury for afternoon tea – something of a mix between smoked salmon sandwiches and freshly baked scones...

2 cup/10 oz/300 g all-purpose/plain flour
1 tbsp baking powder
1 tbsp superfine/caster sugar
½ tsp salt
2¾ oz/75 g cream cheese, plus extra to serve
Generous ¾ cup/7 fl oz/200 ml milk
1 large egg, beaten
¼ cup/2 oz/60 g butter, melted
3½ oz/100 g smoked salmon, snipped into small pieces
2 scallions/spring onions, chopped
1 tsp fresh dill, chopped
Ground black pepper
Fresh dill sprigs to garnish

1 Preheat the oven to 400°F/200°C/ Gas mark 6. Grease or line a 12-hole muffin pan/tin.

2 Mix the flour, baking powder, sugar and salt together and sift into a large bowl.

3 In a separate bowl, beat the cream cheese until soft, then gradually beat in the milk until smooth and creamy. Stir in the egg and butter, followed by the salmon, scallions/ spring onions, dill and a good grinding of black pepper. Pour into the dry ingredients and stir until just combined, then spoon big dollops of the batter into the prepared muffin pan and grind over a little more black pepper.

4 Bake for about 20 minutes until risen and golden. Leave to cool in the pan for a few minutes, then transfer to a wire rack to cool.

5 Serve spread with more cream cheese and dill sprigs to decorate.

KIDS' PARTY MENUS

Kids love parties but planning a fun-filled event AND delicious treats can be a headache. The key is in the preparation ... and having a few clever tricks up your sleeve.

BOYS' PARTY MENU

Chocolate Cake 42

90  Lemon Biscuits

Boys' Own Cupcakes 90

Coloured Candies

Fresh Orange & Apple Juice

Mini packs of raisins make brilliant snacks and tasty party bag fillers.

GIRLS' PARTY MENU

Birthday Mini Muffins

 Rocky Roadsters

Custard Creams

 Butterflies Go Disco

Homemade Lemonade

GO TO THE PAGES LISTED FOR FULL RECIPES AND INSTRUCTIONS.

Party Time!

For more child-friendly cupcakes see *Cupcake Magic* by Kate Shirazi.

Lemony lustres

Edible lustre comes as a powder in tiny tubes from sugarcraft shops.

1 stick/4 oz/110 g butter, softened
½ cup/4 oz/110 g superfine/caster sugar
2 large free-range eggs, beaten
Generous ¾ cup/4 oz/110 g self-rising/-raising flour, sifted
1 tsp baking powder
Grated zest of 1 unwaxed lemon
1 tbsp freshly squeezed lemon juice

FOR THE DECORATION

1 quantity glacé frosting (p.48)
Gel food colouring (optional)
1 tbsp royal icing (see p.48)
Edible lustre (available from cake decorating and sugarcraft shops)
½ tsp vodka or other clear alcohol
You will need a small paintbrush

Preheat the oven to 325°F/170°C/Gas mark 3. Line a 12-hole muffin pan/tin with baking cups/cupcake cases. Cream the butter and sugar together until really pale and fluffy. Slowly add the beaten eggs, beating well after each addition. Sift the flour and baking powder onto the mixture and, using a large metal spoon, carefully fold it in. Add the lemon zest and, if the batter looks a little stiff, add the juice a little at a time (it may not be necessary).

Fold again. The batter should gently plop off the spoon. Spoon into the prepared cases and bake for 20–25 minutes until golden and firm to the touch. Remove from the oven and leave to cool.

Make the glacé frosting (see p.48) and colour as required. Spoon over the cooled cakes. When the frosting has dried, put the royal icing into a decorating/piping bag with a fine tube/nozzle, and pipe a large heart onto each cupcake. Wait for this to harden slightly, which will take around an hour.

To finish, tip ½ tsp of the lustre onto a saucer or into a small bowl. Add some vodka to the lustre drop by drop. Mix with the paintbrush until you have a consistency just a tiny bit looser than a paste. Leave the alcohol to evaporate – the mixture will thicken up slightly. Carefully brush the lustre mixture over the piped heart and let it dry.

Boys' own

I like the idea of a masculine cupcake! Well, if there are cupcakes with frocks and shoes, it's only fair that the chaps should have something. Let us not forget that men are huge consumers of cake, although they may pretend they aren't that bothered.

1 quantity of basic vanilla cupcakes (see p.32)
1 quantity glacé frosting (p.48)
Gel food colouring in assorted colours
2 tbsp royal icing (see p.48)
You will need 3 decorating/piping bags fitted with fine tubes/nozzles

Make the cupcakes according to the recipe and leave to cool.

Make the glacé frosting with the confectioners'/icing sugar and either lemon juice or water. Colour the frosting a really deep blue or green or brown. Cover the cakes with the frosting and let them dry really well. With colour this dark, it is important that the frosting is as dry as possible before you start decorating.

Divide the royal icing into three bowls, and tint them whatever colour the chap likes. The royal icing needs to be really firm, so if it's a bit on the loose side add a little more sifted confectioners' sugar. Pipe on appropriately butch comic-strip type words, such as 'BIFF', 'POW' and 'ZAP'. Word of warning: if you pipe on the words before the frosting underneath has dried, or if the royal icing is too wet, the colours will bleed into each other.

Makes about 12

Makes about 12

Makes 12

Butterflies go disco

I have developed a growing stash of cutters. The glitter butterfly remains a firm favourite.

1 quantity of basic vanilla cupcakes (p.32)
1 quantity glacé frosting (p.48)
Food colouring (preferably gel)
Cornstarch/cornflour for dusting
Golf ball-sized piece of rolled fondant/sugarpaste
Edible glue
Edible glitter
You will need butterfly cutters (large, small or both) and a paintbrush

Make the cupcakes according to whichever recipe you choose, and leave to cool. Make up the glacé frosting (p.16) and colour as you wish. Pour over the cakes and leave to dry.

Dust a little cornstarch/cornflour onto a work surface, and roll out the rolled fondant/sugarpaste until it is about ⅛ in/3 mm thick. Cut out butterflies – allow one large butterfly per cake or two small.

Brush a little edible glue all over the butterflies and dip onto the edible glitter that you have poured onto a plate.

Stick the butterflies to the cakes. If you are using two small ones, it looks lovely if you have them flying off in different directions.

Decorating fun!
For a fun kids' party try baking plain cupcakes and providing the guests with frosting and sprinkles to create their very own masterpieces!

Peanut butter & choc chip cheekies

Kids just love these big fat muffins studded with chocolate chips and little nuggets of peanut. Throw a batch in the oven after school and they can enjoy them warm with a big glass of milk. If you want to go for a dairy-free version, use bittersweet chocolate chips and substitute soya milk for regular milk.

2 cups/10 oz/300 g self-rising/-raising flour
1 tsp baking powder
3½ oz/100 g milk chocolate chips
Generous ⅔ cup/7 oz/200 g crunchy peanut butter
4 oz/⅔ cup/110 g soft brown sugar
2 eggs, beaten
Generous ¾ cup/7 fl oz/200 ml milk

Preheat the oven to 400°F/200°C/Gas mark 6. Grease or line a 12-hole muffin pan/tin.

Combine the flour and baking powder and sift into a large bowl, then add about three-quarters of the chocolate chips.

In a separate bowl, beat together the peanut butter and sugar, then gradually beat in the eggs and milk to make a smooth mixture. Pour into the dry ingredients and stir together until just combined, then spoon large dollops into the prepared muffin pan. Sprinkle with the remaining chocolate chips, pressing them gently into the mixture.

Bake for about 18 minutes until risen and golden. Leave to cool in the pan for a few minutes, then transfer to a wire rack to cool.

Beet bonanza

Don't be put off if you don't like beets, these perfectly pink muffins are not a million miles away from a carrot-cakey muffin – sweet, tender, moreish and, even better, bright pink! Serve them with a simple swirl of frosting or, for something a bit more special, look out for pink sugar sprinkles to scatter over the top.

Makes 12

2 cups/10 oz/300 g all-purpose/plain flour
1 tbsp baking powder
Scant ²/₃ cup/5 oz/150 g superfine/caster sugar
1 tsp ground cinnamon
½ tsp ground ginger
Generous ¾ cup/7 fl oz/200 ml milk
2 large eggs, beaten
Scant ½ cup/3½ fl oz/100 ml vegetable oil
Largish beet/beetroot, grated (about 3½ oz/100 g)

FOR THE FROSTING
5 oz/150 g cream cheese
4½ tbsp confectioners'/icing sugar
1 tsp lemon juice
Pink food colouring

Preheat the oven to 400°F/200°C/Gas mark 6. Grease or line a 12-hole muffin pan/tin.

Combine the flour, baking powder, superfine/caster sugar, cinnamon and ginger and sift into a large bowl.

In a separate bowl, combine the milk, eggs and oil, then stir in the beet so that the mixture turns bright pink. Pour into the dry ingredients and stir together until just combined, then spoon large dollops of the mixture into the prepared muffin pan.

Bake for about 20 minutes until risen and firm to the touch. Leave to cool in the pan for a few minutes, then transfer the muffins to a wire rack to cool.

To serve, beat together the cream cheese, confectioners'/icing sugar and lemon juice until smooth and creamy. Add a few drops of pink food colouring to make a vibrant pink frosting, then swirl on top of the muffins.

Coloured candies

These muffins are kiddie-tastic and will appeal to really little ones as much as older kids – particularly the way the candies turn the muffins rainbow-coloured once they've been baked. Little-uns can help out with spooning on the frosting and sticking on M&Ms, while older kids can pretty much do it all themselves.

Makes 12

2 cups/10 oz/300 g self-rising/-raising flour
1 tsp baking powder
½ cup/4 oz/110 g superfine/caster sugar
2 oz/60 g Smarties or M&Ms
generous ¾ cup/7 fl oz/200 ml buttermilk
1 egg, beaten
1 tsp vanilla extract
Scant ½ cup/3 oz/85 g butter, melted

TO DECORATE
Scant ¹/₃ cup/2½ fl oz/75 ml sour cream
1 cup/3½ oz/100 g confectioners'/icing sugar, sifted
2 oz/60 g Smarties or M&Ms

Preheat the oven to 375°F/190°C/Gas mark 5. Grease or line a 12-hole muffin pan/tin.

Combine the flour, baking powder and superfine/caster sugar and sift into a large bowl, then add the Smarties or M&Ms.

In a separate bowl or jug, lightly beat the buttermilk, egg and vanilla to combine, then stir in the butter. Pour into the dry ingredients and stir together until just combined, then spoon big dollops of the mixture into the prepared muffin pan.

Bake for about 20 minutes until risen and golden. Leave to cool in the pan for a few minutes, then transfer the muffins to a wire rack to cool completely.

To decorate, beat the sour cream and confectioners'/icing sugar together until creamy, then spoon over the muffins. Decorate with more Smarties or M&Ms on top.

Birthday mini muffins

Who needs a birthday cake when there are mini muffins to gobble instead? With twenty-four muffins in each batch, they're just perfect for a party – or for a very greedy birthday boy or girl!

Makes 24

2 cups/10 oz/300 g self-rising/-raising flour
1 tsp baking powder
2 tbsp cocoa powder, plus extra for dusting
²/₃ cup/5 oz/150 g superfine/caster sugar
3½ oz/100 g bittersweet/dark chocolate, chopped
1 egg, beaten
Generous 1 cup/9 fl oz/250 ml plain yogurt
2 tbsp milk
Scant ½ cup/3 oz/85 g butter, melted
24 birthday candles to decorate

Preheat the oven to 375°F/190°C/Gas mark 5. Grease or line a 24-hole mini muffin pan/tin.

Combine the flour, baking powder, cocoa and superfine/caster sugar and sift into a large bowl, then add the chocolate.

In a separate bowl or jug, combine the egg, yogurt, milk and butter, then pour into the dry ingredients. Stir together until just combined, then spoon large dollops of the mixture into the prepared muffin pan, making sure there are plenty of chocolate chunks peeping through the tops of the muffins.

Bake for about 15 minutes until risen and firm to the touch. Leave to cool in the pan for a few minutes, then transfer to a wire rack to cool completely.

To serve, dust with cocoa and stick a candle in the centre of each muffin. Light and enjoy!

For more great muffin ideas see *Muffin Magic* by Susannah Blake

GLUTEN FREE

If you think avoiding gluten or wheat means having to do without delicious cakes and bakes, think again. These recipes are a selection from *HoneyBuns Gluten-free Baking* by Emma Goss Custard, a fabulous collection of gluten-free treat.

Gooseberry fool cake

Makes 1 9 in/23 cm round cake

This gooseberry-laden sponge marries brilliantly with the light-as-a-feather elderflower topping. Its high fruit content means that it's a good source of vitamins A and C. This cake is best made with the really tart, early season green gooseberries. You can use red or yellow varieties, but they are quite a lot sweeter. If fresh gooseberries are hard to find, you can use frozen ones. As it is so moist, this cake needs to be kept in the refrigerator. The frosting will wilt after a day or two – simply re-fluff it with a fork.

⅔ cup/5½ oz/150 g butter, melted, plus extra for brushing
Tapioca flour for dusting
5 eggs
1 cup/7 oz/200 g light brown sugar
2 cups/7 oz/200 g ground almonds
Scant 1 cup/3½ oz/100 g sorghum flour
1½ tsp gluten-free baking powder
1½ tsp guar gum
1 tsp vanilla extract
A pinch of salt
1 lb/450 g green gooseberries, topped, tailed, rinsed and dried

FOR THE FROSTED BERRIES
7 whole gooseberries, topped, tailed, rinsed and dried
1 tbsp pasteurized liquid egg white
1–2 tbsp superfine/caster sugar

FOR THE ELDERFLOWER CREAM
scant 1 cup/7 fl oz/200 ml heavy/double cream
2 tbsp elderflower cordial
⅓ cup/1½ oz/40 g confectioners'/icing sugar, sifted

1 Preheat the oven to 350°F/180°C/Gas mark 4. Line a 9 in/23 cm round springform pan/tin with a disc of parchment paper, then brush with melted butter and dust with tapioca flour.

2 Crack the eggs into a large mixing bowl and beat with an electric mixer on high speed. Add the melted butter and beat again. Add the sugar, almonds, sorghum flour, baking powder, guar gum, vanilla and salt, then beat until creamy. Stir in the gooseberries using a rubber spatula. Be gentle: you want to keep them intact.

3 Spoon the mixture into the prepared pan and bang the pan firmly on a work surface to get rid of air pockets. Bake for 45 minutes until firm and springy to the touch. A flat cake skewer will come out clean when the cake is ready.

4 Leave the cake in its tin for 10–15 minutes, then turn it out, right way up, onto a rack covered with parchment paper. Leave to cool, then peel off the parchment. For the frosted berries, wash the gooseberries and pat them dry. Brush them lightly with egg white, then roll them in superfine/caster sugar. Place the coated berries on a piece of parchment paper and leave to dry.

5 For the elderflower cream topping, whip the cream with the cordial and confectioners'/icing sugar until it forms stiff peaks. Spread the cream over the cake with a palette knife: we like a rough peaked finish, but you could go super-sleek. Decorate with the frosted berries.

Raspberry & white chocolate cake

This is simple to make, perfect for a summer's day. Once the topping is on, the cake should be quickly admired and then eaten before the cream slides off.

Melted butter for brushing
Tapioca flour for dusting
4 eggs
¾ cup/5½ oz/150 g light brown sugar
1¾ cups/4½ oz/125 g hazelnuts, ground
Scant ½ cup/1¾ oz/50 g cornmeal/polenta
¼ cup/1 oz/25 g sorghum flour
1½ tsp gluten-free baking powder
1½ tsp guar gum and ¼ tsp salt
Generous 1 cup/2¾ oz/75 g hazelnuts, toasted and chopped
5½ oz/150 g white chocolate, chopped
5–6 tbsp top-quality raspberry jam for filling
24 raspberries to decorate

FOR THE ROASTED RASPBERRIES
7 oz/200 g raspberries
4 tbsp clear honey
½ tsp cinnamon sugar

FOR THE CREAM FILLING & TOPPING
Generous 1 cup/7 oz/200 g mascarpone
⅓ cup/3½ fl oz/100 ml heavy/double cream
3½ oz/½ cup/100 g crème fraîche
2 oz/½ cup/60 g confectioners'/icing sugar
2 tsp lemon juice and 1 tsp vanilla extract

FOR THE EASPBERRY SUGAR
1 freeze-dried raspberry
1 tsp confectioners'/icing sugar

1 Preheat the oven to 350°F/180°C/ Gas mark 4. Brush 2 x 8 in/20 cm round shallow cake pans/tins with melted butter and dust with tapioca flour.

2 For the roasted raspberries, put the berries in a baking pan, drizzle the honey over them and dredge with cinnamon sugar. Roast in the oven for 20 minutes. Leave to cool for 5 minutes.

3 Crack the eggs into a large bowl, then add the sugar, ground nuts, cornmeal/polenta, sorghum flour, baking powder, guar gum and salt. Beat with an electric mixer until creamy and stiff. Using a spatula, stir in the chopped nuts, white chocolate and roasted raspberries.

4 Divide the mixture between the pans. Bake for 20–25 minutes, until a flat cake skewer comes out clean. Leave the cakes in the pans for a couple of minutes, then turn out onto a rack. Invert one so its flat bottom side is upwards.

5 For the cream filling, put the mascarpone, cream, crème fraîche, confectioners'/icing sugar, lemon juice and vanilla into a bowl and beat with an electric mixer until stiff.

6 For the raspberry sugar, use the back of a spoon to crush the freeze-dried raspberry to a fine powder. Sift in the 1 tsp confectioners' sugar – if it is not pink enough, add a little more raspberry. Only mix little by little as you need it, as the freeze-dried raspberry goes soft after a couple of hours.

7 Spread 1 cake thickly with raspberry jam. Spread half the cream filling on top of the jam and place the second cake on top. Spread the remaining cream filling on top of the cake. Arrange the raspberries on top and dust the cake with raspberry sugar.

Makes
1
2 lb/900 g
loaf
cake

Upside-down polenta plum cake

This is a great cake for using up any bumper seasonal fruit harvests. Instead of plums you could use damsons or peaches – or any fruit with a bit of body. The great thing about red-skinned plums (we use Victoria plums) is that you benefit from the gorgeous colour contrast against the sunshine yellow of the cornmeal. The cake itself is not very sweet, but when it is turned upside down those lovely syrupy fruit juices seep into the sponge. Delicious served warm with homemade custard (see page 147).

Scant ½ cup/3½ oz/100 g butter, melted, plus extra for brushing
2 eggs
1½ cups/6½ oz/185 g cornmeal/polenta
⅔ cup/2¼ oz/70 g ground almonds
1½ tsp gluten-free baking powder
¾ tsp guar gum
¾ tsp vanilla extract
6½ oz/185 g rice syrup
Scant 1 cup/7 oz/200 g crème fraîche
2 tbsp orange juice

FOR THE TOPPING
8 red plums, halved and pitted
4 tbsp light brown sugar
⅓ cup/3½ fl oz/100 ml orange juice

1. Preheat the oven to 350°F/180°C/ Gas mark 4. Brush a 2 lb/900 g loaf pan/tin with melted butter, line with a silicone loaf pan liner, then liberally butter the loaf liner.

2. First, make the topping. Put the plums, skin side up, in a baking pan. Mix the brown sugar and orange juice and pour over the plums. Roast in the oven for about 15–17 minutes, until soft but still keeping their shape. Cool in the pan.

3. Crack the eggs into a large bowl, then add the cornmeal/polenta, almonds, baking powder, guar gum and vanilla extract. In another bowl, mix the melted butter with the rice syrup, crème fraîche and orange juice. Beat with an electric mixer at low speed until just combined. Don't worry if it looks a bit curdled. Pour this mixture over the dry ingredients and beat at high speed until smooth and pale.

4. Take the plums out of the pan and put them in the loaf pan, skin side down. Pour the syrup that remains in the baking pan into a measuring cup or jug and pour 4 tsp of the syrup over the plums in the loaf pan. Set the rest aside.

5. Spoon the cake mixture into the loaf pan and spread it gently. Bake for 30 minutes, then cover with a disc of parchment paper and bake for a further 15–20 minutes until springy to the touch; a flat cake skewer will come out clean when the cake is ready. As soon as the cake comes out of the oven, loosen the sides with a knife, then place a serving plate upside down on top of the pan and turn over quickly. Remove from the pan and peel off the parchment paper. Spoon the remaining syrup from cooking the plums over the cake while it is still warm.

Custard creams

Makes 16 cookies

We do love the classic British custard creams; here, we've reinterpreted them in fabulous gluten-free form.

1½ sticks/5½ oz/150 g butter, softened and cubed
¾ cup/5½ oz/150 g superfine/caster sugar
1¼ cups/5½ oz/150 g cornmeal/polenta
Generous 1½ cups/5½ oz/150 g ground almonds
Scant ¾ cup/3½ oz/100 g custard powder
1 egg
½ tsp vanilla extract
Tapioca flour for dusting

FOR THE FILLING
1¼ sticks/9 oz/250 g butter, softened
¾ cup/3½ oz/100 g confectioners'/icing sugar
2 tbsp custard powder
½ tsp vanilla extract

TO DECORATE
1–2 tbsp confectioners'/icing sugar, sifted
You will need a decorating/piping bag fitted with a small star tube/nozzle

1 Preheat the oven to 325°F/170°C/Gas mark 3. Cut pieces of baking parchment to line the base of two large baking sheets.

2 Put the butter, sugar, cornmeal/polenta, almonds, custard powder, egg and vanilla into a large mixing bowl and beat using an electric mixer at low speed until the mixture forms a soft dough.

3 Dust your hands, rolling pin and work surface lightly with tapioca flour. Knead the dough gently and then roll out to about ¼ in/5 mm thick. Using a pastry cutter (we used a 2½ in/6 cm heart-shaped cutter), cut out the dough and place the shapes on the baking sheets. The cookies will spread as they bake, so make sure you leave plenty of space between them.

4 Bake for 12–14 minutes, until golden and firm to the touch (they get firmer as they cool). Leave on the baking sheets for 5–10 minutes, then transfer to a wire rack.

5 To make the filling, put the butter into a bowl. Sift the confectioners'/icing sugar and custard powder into the bowl, add the vanilla and beat using an electric mixer at medium speed until smooth. Chill in the refrigerator for 30 minutes.

6 Spoon the filling into a decorating bag/piping fitted with a small star tube/nozzle. Turn half of the cookies upside down and pipe the cream in swirls on top. Cover with the remaining cookies – with the nice side facing upwards.

7 To decorate, place a paper doily over the cookies and dust with confectioners' sugar.

Cranberry, pecan & maple syrup flapjacks

These are generously laden with pecans, and the maple syrup marries really well with both the pecans and the cranberries. It really is worth going to the effort of toasting the pecans.

Generous 1½ sticks/6½ oz/185 g butter, plus extra, melted, for brushing
Generous ½ cup/4 oz/110 g light brown sugar
3½ tbsp/2½ oz/70 g corn/golden syrup
3 tbsp maple syrup
½ tsp salt
Generous 1¾ cups/5½ oz/150 g gluten-free oats
3½ oz/100 g gluten-free oat flour
1 cup/3½ oz/100 g pecan halves, toasted
½ cup/1¾ oz/50 g pecan halves, toasted and chopped
3 oz/85 g millet flakes
Generous ½ cup/2½ oz/70 g dried cranberries
Finely grated zest of 1 orange
½ tsp orange oil

FOR THE TOPPING
3 tbsp/1 oz/25 g dried cranberries
Finely grated zest of 1 orange
3 tbsp maple syrup

1 Preheat the oven to 325°F/170°C/Gas mark 3. Cut a rectangle of parchment paper to line the base of a 12 × 9 × 1½ in/30 × 23 × 4 cm baking pan/tin. Pop the parchment in the pan and brush it and the pan liberally with melted butter.

2 Put the butter, sugar, corn/golden syrup, maple syrup and salt into a pan and melt over a low heat, stirring every minute or so with a wooden spoon. Cook for 8–10 minutes until all the sugar has dissolved (when the bottom of the pan no longer feels gritty, the mixture is ready). Don't let the mixture boil or the flapjacks will be hard.

3 Put the oats, oat flour, halved and chopped pecans, millet flakes, dried cranberries, orange zest and orange oil into a large bowl and stir. Pour in the melted butter mixture and stir well, using a rubber spatula. Ensure that all the dry ingredients are well coated.

4 Spoon the mixture into the pan and spread evenly, using a rubber spatula – you need to push it into the corners, but leave the surface fairly lumpy for a rustic effect. For the topping, scatter the cranberries over the surface, pressing them in lightly.

5 Bake for 15–17 minutes until golden with slightly darker edges. It will be bubbling and quite soft when you take it from the oven, but will firm up as it cools. Leave in the pan to cool for 10 minutes, then transfer to a wire rack.

6 Mix the grated orange zest with the maple syrup and drizzle it over the flapjack while it is still warm. Cut up into 15 slices.

FLOUR POWER

The flour we are all familiiar with is milled from wheat grains – but it can be made from all kinds of different starchy grains, which is good news for those of us intolerant of wheat and gluten.

Chestnut flour

Chestnut flour has a natural sweetness and nutty flavour. It works particularly well in dense, chocolatey cakes. It's available from larger supermarkets and specialist food shops, and online.

Gram/chickpea flour

Use this sparingly, as it can leave a slightly bitter aftertaste. However, it's great blended with other flours in savoury pastries. Readily available online and from Asian food stores.

Coconut flour

Coconut flour has a dominant flavour, which works well where you want a coconut flavour, but it's not generally interchangeable with other flours.

Cornstarch/cornflour

Cornstarch is great in shortbreads as it lends a 'melt-in-the-mouth' quality. Best used blended with other flours, as it hasn't enough body to be used on its own.

Linseed/Flaxseed (brown, ground)

The nutty, sweet flavour and high moisture content of this flour makes it a really delicious ingredient. It is often interchangeable with sorghum, millet and gluten-free oat flours. It is available from health food shops and from some supermarkets 'free from' ranges, or online.

Hazelnut flour

Hazelnut meal flour is available online. Alternatively, you can toast and grind your own nuts.

Millet flour

Allergycare millet flour is available from various online suppliers.

Oats and oat flour

Strictly gluten-free oats and gluten-free oat flour can be difficult to source due to possible contamination from wheat or other cereals in the field or mill – and some celiacs are sensitive even to pure oats. Millet flour and millet flakes are a good alternative if you'd prefer to avoid oats.

Polenta

For baking, use dry, finely ground cornmeal (not the pre-cooked polenta blocks). It's great mixed with other flours or ground nuts.

Quinoa flour

Quinoa isn't technically a grain, but a seed, and is incredibly nutritious. The flour is available online and in some health food shops.

Rice flour

Brown rice flour is available online and in some health food shops and supermarkets. Glutinous rice flour is also gluten-free: 'glutinous' refers to the stickiness of the rice. Available from Asian food stores and online.

Sorghum flour/juwar

This fabulous flour produces a lovely fluffy cake texture and can be used blended or on its own. Available from Asian food stores, or online.

Cassava/tapioca flour

Tapioca flour is similar to cornstarch: it's very soft and neutral in flavour. Best used blended with other flours. It is available in health food shops and online.

For comprehensive guidance and a whole host of delicious recipes using gluten-free ingredients check out Emma Goss Custard's *Honeybuns Gluten-free Baking*

Gluten-free baking

Gluten-free cooking can be exciting and creative, and the results utterly gorgeous. Just like any other cooking, in fact. Some of the ingredients may sound strange at first, but once you get to know them you'll be able to run with them. It's best to focus on what can be done – brilliantly – with the resources available. Don't worry about being able to 'translate' traditional recipes to gluten free precisely… down this path disappointment and vexation lie.

Gluten-free ingredients

Inspiration from Northern Italy includes polenta, and toasted and ground nuts such as almonds, pistachios and hazelnuts, where these ingredients are commonly used. Ground nuts have a softer texture and higher moisture content than rice flours and typical gluten-free flour mixes. Rice flour is a useful ingredient, but only in combination with other flours. For cakes will last longer than just a day or two, the natural oiliness of ground nuts helps keep them moist. Ground linseed/flax seed is less expensive than many nuts, however, and can be used to replace some or all of the nuts in a recipe. Linseed has a naturally nutty flavour and a sweetness, and behaves in much the same way as ground almonds in cooking. Sorghum flour and tapioca flour are soft and absorbent, resulting in light, fluffy cakes. Steer clear of potato-derived flours as they can be heavy, and use gram flour/chickpea flour sparingly as it can have a slightly sour taste. Gluten-free oats and oat flour are great for adding texture, but check that they are certified gluten-free, as this is not always the case.

Tips and techniques

Gluten lends stretch and 'glue' to a mixture. In certain cake recipes, the lack of gluten is not so critical. For example, you can achieve a wonderfully textured brownie using ground almonds in place of wheat flour. Pastry, however, is more of a challenge to create without gluten. When making cakes, brownies and other beaten batters, ensure your ingredients are at room temperature and not straight from the refrigerator. If you add anything too hot or too cold it can cause the mixture to shrink during cooking.

If your mixture includes beaten eggs, be careful not to pour warm melted butter or chocolate directly onto the eggs, as the heat may cause them to scramble. If baking powder comes into contact with anything acidic, it may react and cause the mixture to separate, so it's a good idea to keep it insulated from acidic ingredients such as lemon or orange juice, zest or oil, rhubarb or other acidic fruit. When adding ingredients to a mixing bowl, always 'sandwich' the baking powder between other dry ingredients.

Pastry

Pastry dough without gluten requires a little TLC. All pastries are easier to handle if chilled in the refrigerator for an hour or so before rolling out. Using a liberal dusting of tapioca flour and rolling pastry mixes between sheets of silicone paper are nifty tricks. With butter-based pastries and crusts you need to work with chilled and cubed or grated butter.

In warmer weather you'll often end up with a stickier dough and in colder weather you may need to mix it for longer and hand-mould it into something workable. You just need the confidence to manually handle it and swiftly squidge it into shape. Sometimes you may need to add a little milk or egg yolk as a binder. Pastry is more vulnerable to variables than other forms of baking: room temperature, moisture levels and your body temperature all have an effect. Once you've made the mixtures a couple of times you'll get a feel for what to adjust. Sometimes the recipe asks you to bake the pastry blind; this works well in gluten-free pastry without a need for baking beans or parchment paper.

SAINTLY TREATS

Sometimes you need to rein in those calories, and let's face it, most cakes aren't too easy on the waistline. Here are some examples of really healthy, satisfying snacks that will give you a nutrient boost but still feel like a treat – and won't break the calorie bank if you're watching your weight.

Makes 1 batch

Soft berry cookies

These are just the most delicious, fruit-packed, oaty, soft cookies. They are easy to make and you can alter the fruit to whatever you can get your hands on. Health food stores and now most supermarkets sell a vast array of dried tropical fruit. I've made them with dried mangoes, raisins, figs, blueberries, pears – all work beautifully.

Makes 1 batch

Generous ¼ cup/2½ fl oz/60 ml sunflower oil
6 tbsp/3 oz/85 g butter, softened
½ cup/4 oz/110 g soft light brown sugar
1 large free-range egg
½ tsp vanilla extract
¾ cup/4 oz/100 g jumbo oats
Scant 1 cup/5 oz/140 g plain whole-wheat/wholemeal flour
½ tsp baking soda/bicarbonate of soda
½ tsp baking powder
½ tsp ground cinnamon
4 oz/110 g dried apple
1 oz/25 g cranberries
1 oz/25 g blueberries

Preheat the oven to 350°F/180°C/Gas mark 4 and line two baking sheets with silicone liners.

Mix the sunflower oil, butter and sugar together in a large bowl. Beat in the egg and vanilla, then stir in the oats. Sift the flour, baking soda/bicarbonate of soda, baking powder and cinnamon over the sugar and oil mixture and mix in. Add the dried fruit and stir until they are just combined.

Drop dessertspoonfuls of the mixture onto your lined baking sheets, leaving lots of space between them as they spread and bake for about 10 minutes until pale golden. Leave on the baking sheets to harden and set a bit before cooling on wire racks.

No-bake healthy humdingers

This has got to be the ultimate in virtuous cookies. Yet again, I am pushing the boundaries about what actually constitutes a cookie. These aren't even cooked, for goodness' sake. There is not one ingredient here that a full-on health food addict would have a problem with, and they are actually great as sports snacks too, as they fill a gap and have lots of lovely slow-release sugar properties. Perfect.

Makes 1 batch

½ cup/4½ oz/125 g sunflower seeds
1 tbsp tahini (sesame seed paste)
¹/₃ cup/2 oz/60 g dry unsweetened/desiccated or shredded coconut
1 tbsp runny honey
1½ oz/40 g wheatgerm
2 oz/60 g dates, pitted and chopped

Bash the sunflower seeds a little in a mortar with a pestle or in a food processor. You just want to break them up a bit. Tip them into a large bowl and add all the other ingredients. Form the mixture (easier to do this in 2 portions) into a roll, wrap tightly in plastic wrap and leave to chill in the refrigerator for a couple of hours. When you are ready, just slice pieces off.

Bananas-a-go-go cookies

Right, these little chaps are pretty cool. Really easy to make, they are sugar and wheat free, the fat is 'healthy' fat, and they are really banana-y! They are soft cookies, so if you are waiting for them to crisp up, you may be waiting a while, and they are also best eaten on the day you make them.

Makes 1 batch

3 ripe bananas
6½ oz/180 g pitted dates, chopped
1 cup/5½ oz/150 g rolled jumbo oats
¹/₃ cup/3 fl oz/80 ml sunflower oil
1 tsp vanilla extract

Preheat the oven to 350°F/180°C/Gas mark 4 and line two baking sheets with silicone liners.

Mash the bananas in a large bowl, then add the dates, oats, sunflower oil and vanilla, and give it a good mix. Leave the mixture to stand for 15–20 minutes to firm up a little and for the oats to absorb some of the liquid.

Drop teaspoons of the mixture onto your lined baking sheets and flatten with the back of a spoon – they don't spread much, so the shape you make on the sheet will be the shape of the finished cookie. Bake for 15–20 minutes then transfer the cookies to a wire rack to cool.

Try making cookies or bars packed with seeds and dried fruit for travel snacks, or even as on-the-run breakfast fixes for busy days.

Chewy date cookies

Dates are just fantastic in cooking, and their intense sweetness means that you can reduce the amount of sugar you add to the recipe. These date lovelies still contain sugar, as it's important for the chewy factor. You can reduce the amount of sugar you use, but it will change the overall consistency. You could also use entirely whole-wheat flour instead of a mixture of white and brown. It is up to you.

Makes 1 batch

¾ stick/3 oz/75 g butter, softened
¾ cup/5 oz/140 g soft light brown sugar
Finely grated zest of 1 large unwaxed lemon
1 large free-range egg
Generous ¾ cup/4 oz/110 g all-purpose/plain flour
½ cup/3½ oz/80 g whole-wheat/wholemeal flour
1 tsp baking powder
½ tsp grated nutmeg
1 tsp ground cinnamon
A pinch of salt
¼ cup/2 fl oz/60 ml milk
6½ oz/180 g pitted dates, chopped

Preheat the oven to 325°F/170°C/Gas mark 3 and line two baking sheets with silicone liners.

Cream the butter and sugar together in a large bowl until light and fluffy, then add the zest and egg and beat away. In another bowl, sift together the flours, baking powder, nutmeg, cinnamon and salt. Add to the creamed mixture in alternate dollops with a little bit of milk and beat well between each addition. Finally stir in the dates. Drop round dessertspoons of the mixture onto your lined baking sheets, leaving space between them as they spread, and bake for 12–15 minutes until golden brown. Transfer the cookies to wire racks to cool.

Maple cloud cookies

These cookies have a light and fluffy texture — something between a soft cookie and a muffin. I have included them because they are sugar free, and are suitable for those who are sugar-intolerant and diabetics, who often get ignored in the homemade cookie department. Sugar substitutes can be found in all supermarkets nowadays. It's usually in the sugar aisle.

Makes 1 batch

1 stick/4 oz/110 g butter, softened (although if push comes to shove you could use something like a soy margarine)
½ cup/4 oz/110 g sour cream
4½ oz/125 g apple, peeled and grated
2 large free-range eggs
1 tsp maple syrup
½ tsp vanilla extract
1¾ cups/9 oz/250 g all-purpose/plain flour
⅓ cup/2½ oz/65 g sugar substitute
1 tsp baking soda/bicarbonate of soda
1 tsp baking powder

Preheat the oven to 375°F/190°C/Gas mark 5 and line two baking sheets with silicone liners.

Mix the butter, sour cream, apple, eggs, maple syrup and vanilla together in a large bowl. In another bowl, sift in the flour, sugar substitute, baking soda/bicarbonate of soda and baking powder, then add the dry ingredients to the wet ingredients and mix very well. Drop dessertspoons of the mixture onto your lined baking sheets and bake for about 10 minutes until pale golden. Transfer the cookies to wire racks to cool.

Peter Rabbit cookies

Well, carrot cookies really. Fruit and vegetables in one cookie? Can this be true? Yes, I tell you, yes. Not at all 'worthy'-tasting: carrot and ginger, crystallized papaya, cinnamon and a little hint of coconut, all make these truly delicious little morsels. I'm just going to have another one actually …

Makes 1 batch

7 oz/200 g raw carrots, peeled and chopped
8 tbsp/4 oz/110 g hard white vegetable fat
1 stick/4 oz/110 g butter, softened
¾ cup/4¾ oz/130 g soft light brown sugar
1 large free-range egg
2 cups/10 oz/300 g all-purpose/plain flour
1 tsp baking powder
1 tsp ground cinnamon
1 tsp ground ginger
½ cup/3½ oz/80 g dry unsweetened/desiccated or shredded coconut
2 oz/60 g candied/crystallized papaya

Cook the carrots in a pan of unsalted boiling water until tender and then purée in a blender. You need to avoid any lumps at all, so push it through a sieve if you are unsure whether your purée is smooth enough. Leave to cool until cold.

Preheat the oven to 400°F/200°C/Gas mark 6 and line two baking sheets with silicone liners.

Beat the white fat, butter and sugar together in a large bowl. You may need to scrape the white fat off the bowl every now and again, as it does like to stick to the sides. When the mixture is looking pale and fluffy, add the egg and continue beating until everything is well amalgamated. Add the cold puréed carrots and mix in.

Sift the flour, baking powder, cinnamon and ginger onto the mixture and mix until incorporated. Finally mix in the coconut and papaya. Drop heaped teaspoons onto your lined baking sheets, then flatten and squidge them into thinnish circles with the back of a spoon. Bake for about 10 minutes until golden, then transfer to a wire rack to cool. Delicious.

Mildon flapjacks

Flapjacks are just pushing the boundary of what is or what isn't a cookie, but my reckoning is that you would eat them as you would a cookie, so here they are. Thanks to my friend Helen who gave me her recipe. It's one where you get what, to my mind, is a proper flapjack – still slightly chewy and moist. Very comforting and the oats are amazingly good for you. We'll skip over the other ingredients' health benefits. But they must be good for your mental health. Surely …

Makes 1 batch

Generous 1¼ sticks/9 oz/250 g butter
1¼ cups/9 oz/250 g superfine/caster sugar
½ cup/6 oz/175 g corn/golden syrup
3¼ cups/1 lb 2 oz/500 g jumbo oats

Preheat the oven to 350°F/180°C/Gas mark 4 and grease an 8 in/20 cm square baking pan/tin (if it's a bit bigger or rectangular, please don't worry, just go for it).

Melt the butter, sugar and corn/golden syrup in a large pan. When melted, add the oats and stir in, then tip the whole lot into the pan and press down firmly. Bake for about 25 minutes until pale golden. It may look slightly undercooked and very soft, but it sets as it cools. The key is not to overcook the flapjack, as this way it remains chewy. If you cook it too much, it will be harder. When the flapjack comes out of the oven, quickly score it into pieces with a sharp knife and leave to cool in the pan.

For more delicious treats pick up a copy of *Cookie Magic* by Kate Shirazi

A–Z OF RECIPES

Photographs from Honeybuns by Christian Barnett.
Photographs from Cake Magic by Emma Solley.
Photographs from Cookie Magic and Cupcake Magic by Charlotte Barton.
Photographs from Countrywise Country Cookbook by Kristin Perers.
Photographs from Muffin Magic by Yuki Sugiyura.
Photographs from Good Old-fashioned Teatime Baking by Tara Fisher.

You will find more marvellous recipes in these great books

irresistible recipes for individual treats
Susannah Blake

muffin *magic*

9781862058484

little cakes with attitude
Kate Shirazi

cupcake *magic*

9781862058101

by Kate Shirazi
with Susannah Blake

BAKING *magic*

9781862058897

delicious little bites to bake
Kate Shirazi

cookie *magic*

9781862058477

Kate Shirazi

CAKE *magic*

9781862059177

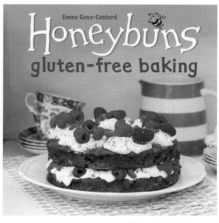

Emma Goss-Custard

Honeybuns
gluten-free baking

9781862059474

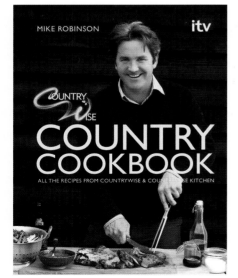

MIKE ROBINSON   itv

COUNTRYWISE
**COUNTRY
COOKBOOK**
ALL THE RECIPES FROM COUNTRYWISE & COUNTRYWISE KITCHEN

9781862059320

These books can be ordered directly
from www.anovabooks.com or try your
local book store.

KEEP
CALM
AND
BAKE

TRADITIONAL RECIPES LOVED BY ALL THE FAMILY

Is produced by Anova Books
Volume Copyright © Anova Books
Old Magistrates Court
10 Southcombe Street
London
W14 0RA

Conversion Charts

Conversions

Weight	Liquid measure	Length	Temperature
½ oz/10 g	1fl oz/30 ml	¼ in/0.5 cm	225°F, 110°C, gas mark ¼
1 oz/25 g	2fl oz/60 ml	½ in/1 cm	250°F, 120°C, gas mark ½
2 oz/60 g	3fl oz/85 ml	¾ in/1.5 cm	275°F, 140°C, gas mark 1
3 oz/85 g	4fl oz/120 ml	1 in/2.5 cm	300°F, 150°C, gas mark 2
4 oz/110 g	5fl oz/150 ml	2 in/5 cm	325°F, 160°C, gas mark 3
5 oz/140 g	10fl oz/300 ml	3 in/7.5 cm	350°F, 180°C, gas mark 4
6 oz/175 g	12fl oz/360 ml	4 in/10 cm	375°F, 190°C, gas mark 5
7 oz/200 g	15fl oz/450 ml	5 in/12.5 cm	400°F, 200°C, gas mark 6
8 oz/225 g	20fl oz/600 ml	6 in/15 cm	425°F, 220°C, gas mark 7
9 oz/250 g		7 in/17.5 cm	450°F, 230°C, gas mark 8
10 oz/280 g		8 in/20 cm	475°F, 240°C, gas mark 9
11 oz/310 g		9 in/22.5 cm	
12 oz/340 g		10 in/25 cm	
13 oz/370 g		11 in/27.5 cm	
14 oz/400 g		12 in/30 cm	
15 oz/425 g			
1 lb/450 g			
1½ lb/675 g			
2 lb/900 g			

These approximate conversions are used throughout this bookazine.
Use a standard cup for measuring.

Cup conversions

Dry measures

1 cup	2 oz/60 g	breadcrumbs; cake crumbs
1 cup	3 oz/85 g	porridge or rolled oats
1 cup	3½ oz/100 g	ground almonds; shredded coconut
1 cup	4 oz/110 g	roughly chopped walnuts and other nuts; confectioners'/icing sugar; cocoa; drinking chocolate; slivered/flaked almonds; grated Cheddar cheese
1 cup	5 oz/140 g	white flour; currants; rice flour; muesli; cornstarch/cornflour; chopped dates; mixed candied peel
1 cup	6 oz/175 g	whole-wheat/wholemeal flour; oatmeal; raisins; golden raisins/sultanas; dried apricots
1 cup	7 oz/200 g	superfine/caster sugar; soft brown sugar; demerara sugar; rice; candied cherries; semolina; chopped figs
1 cup	8 oz/225 g	granulated sugar; curd cheese; cream cheese
1 cup	11 oz/310 g	mincemeat; marmalade; jam
1 cup	12 oz/340 g	corn/golden syrup; blackstrap molasses/treacle

Liquid measures

⅛ cup	1 fl oz	30 ml
¼ cup	2 fl oz	60 ml
½ cup	4 fl oz	120 ml
1 cup	8 fl oz	240 ml
1¼ cups	10 fl oz	300 ml
1½ cups	12 fl oz	360 ml
2 cups	16 fl oz	480 ml
2½ cups	20 fl oz	600 ml

Measures for fats

¼ stick	1 oz	25 g
1 stick	4 oz	110 g

Edexcel GCSE

Mathematics B
Foundation

Student Book
Unit 1

Series Director: Keith Pledger
Series Editor: Graham Cumming

Authors:
Julie Bolter
Gareth Cole
Gill Dyer
Michael Flowers
Karen Hughes
Peter Jolly
Joan Knott
Jean Linsky
Graham Newman
Rob Pepper
Joe Petran
Keith Pledger
Rob Summerson
Kevin Tanner
Brian Western

Published by Pearson Education Limited, a company incorporated in England and Wales, having its registered office at Edinburgh Gate, Harlow, Essex, CM20 2JE. Registered company number: 872828

Edexcel is a registered trademark of Edexcel Limited

Text © Pearson Education Limited 2010

First published 2010

13 12 11 10
10 9 8 7 6 5 4 3 2 1

British Library Cataloguing in Publication Data
A catalogue record for this book is available from the British Library.

ISBN 978 1 846900 96 9

Typeset by Tech-Set Ltd, Gateshead
Picture research by Rebecca Sodergren
Printed in Great Britain at Scotprint, Haddington

Acknowledgements
The author and publisher would like to thank the following individuals and organisations for permission to reproduce photographs:

(Key: b-bottom; c-centre; l-left; r-right; t-top)
Alamy Images: Vito Arcomano 140-141; **Getty Images**: Farjana K. Godhuly 25; **iStockphoto**: 53, 141; Stuart Monk 83; Jack Puccio 138-139; **Jupiter Unlimited**: 138br, 138bl; **Photolibrary.com**: Foodfolio Foodfolio/Imagestate 1; **Science Photo Library Ltd**: Reed Timmer 106; ICP 141tl; Justin Kase Zsixz 141br; **shutterstock**: Lisa F Young 141tr

All other images © Pearson Education

We are grateful to the following for permission to reproduce copyright material:

Tables
Table on page 3 from NHL Team names and statistics, 08–09 season, http://www.nhl.com/ice/app, NHL and NHL Team marks are the property of the NHL and its teams. Copyright © NHL 2010. All Rights Reserved. Used with permission. Table on page 16 (top) adapted from 'UK population figures 1981-2021', Crown Copyright material is reproduced with the permission of the Controller, Office of Public Sector Information (OPSI).; Table on page 16 (bottom) adapted from 'Weather in Aspatria, Cumbria Jan-Oct', Crown Copyright material is reproduced with the permission of the Controller, Office of Public Sector Information (OPSI).

Every effort has been made to contact copyright holders of material reproduced in this book. Any omissions will be rectified in subsequent printings if notice is given to the publishers.

Contents

About this book

All set to make the grade!

Edexcel GCSE Mathematics is specially written to help you get your best grade in the exams.

Recap with a skills check at the start of a section – make sure you're up to speed.

Section objectives show what you'll be learning.

Loads of practice to help you feel secure before you move on.

Graded questions – so you know what you're achieving.

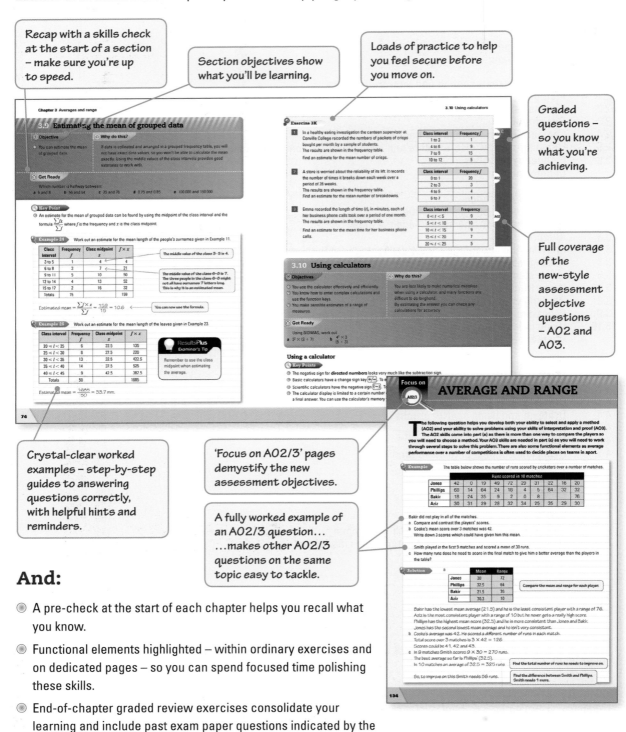

Full coverage of the new-style assessment objective questions – AO2 and AO3.

Crystal-clear worked examples – step-by-step guides to answering questions correctly, with helpful hints and reminders.

'Focus on AO2/3' pages demystify the new assessment objectives.

A fully worked example of an AO2/3 question... ...makes other AO2/3 questions on the same topic easy to tackle.

And:

- A pre-check at the start of each chapter helps you recall what you know.

- Functional elements highlighted – within ordinary exercises and on dedicated pages – so you can spend focused time polishing these skills.

- End-of-chapter graded review exercises consolidate your learning and include past exam paper questions indicated by the month and year.

About ActiveTeach

Use **ActiveTeach** to view and present the course on screen with exciting interactive content.

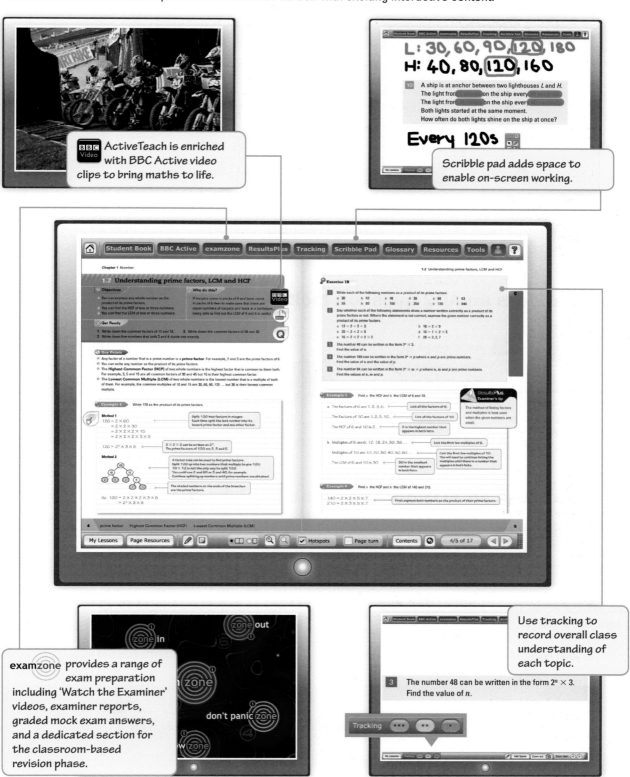

ActiveTeach is enriched with BBC Active video clips to bring maths to life.

Scribble pad adds space to enable on-screen working.

examzone provides a range of exam preparation including 'Watch the Examiner' videos, examiner reports, graded mock exam answers, and a dedicated section for the classroom-based revision phase.

Use tracking to record overall class understanding of each topic.

About Assessment Objectives

Assessment Objectives define the types of question that are set in the exam.

Assessment Objective	What it is	What this means	Range % of marks in the exam
A01	**Recall** and use knowledge of the prescribed content.	Standard questions testing your knowledge of each topic.	45-55
A02	**Select** and apply mathematical methods in a range of contexts.	Deciding what method you need to use to get to the correct solution to a contextualised problem.	25-35
A03	**Interpret** and analyse problems and generate strategies to solve them.	Solving problems by deciding how and explaining why.	15-25

The proportion of marks available in the exam varies with each Assessment Objective. Don't miss out, make sure you know how to do AO2 and AO3 questions!

What does an AO2 question look like?

D **A02**

> This just needs you to
> (a) read and understand the question and
> (b) decide how to get the correct answer.

16 Katie wants to buy a car.
She decides to borrow £3500 from her father. She adds interest of 3.5% to the loan and this total is the amount she must repay her father. How much will Katie pay back to her father in total?

What does an AO3 question look like?

D **A03**

> Here you need to read and analyse the question. Then use your mathematical knowledge to solve this problem.

17 Rashida wishes to invest £2000 in a building society account for one year. The Internet offers two suggestions. Which of these two investments gives Rashida the greatest return?

CHESTMAN BUILDING SOCIETY	DUNSTAN BUILDING SOCIETY
£3.50 per month Plus **1% bonus** at the end of the year	**4%** per annum. Paid yearly by cheque

 Focus on **A02/3**   We give you extra help with AO2 and AO3 on pages 132-137.

About functional elements

What does a question with functional maths look like?

Functional maths is about being able to apply maths in everyday, real-life situations.

GCSE Tier	Range % of marks in the exam
Foundation	30-40
Higher	20-30

The proportion of functional maths marks in the GCSE exam depends on which tier you are taking. Don't miss out, make sure you know how to do functional maths questions!

In the exercises…

20 The Wildlife Trust are doing a survey into the number of field mice on a farm of size 240 acres. They look at one field of size 6 acres. In this field they count 35 field mice.

a Estimate how many field mice there are on the whole farm.

b Why might this be an unreliable estimate?

> You need to read and understand the question. Follow your plan.
>
> Think what maths you need and plan the order in which you'll work.
>
> Check your calculations and make a comment if required.

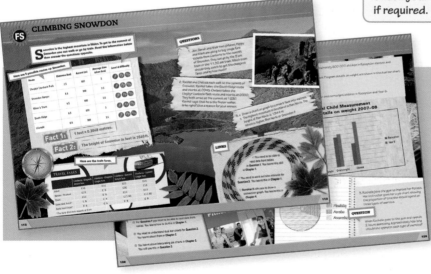

…and on our special functional maths pages:138-141!

Quality of written communication

There will be marks in the exam for showing your working 'properly' and explaining clearly. In the exam paper, such questions will be marked with a star (*). You need to:

- use the correct mathematical notation and vocabulary, to show that you can communicate effectively
- organise the relevant information logically.

ResultsPlus

ResultsPlus features combine exam performance data with examiner insight to give you more information on how to succeed. ResultsPlus tips in the **student books** show students how to avoid errors in solutions to questions.

ResultsPlus
Watch Out!

Some students use the term average – make sure you specify mean, mode or median.

This warns you about common mistakes and misconceptions that examiners frequently see students make.

ResultsPlus
Exam Question Report

91% of students scored poorly on this question because they did not use the midpoint of the range to find the mean of grouped data.

This gives a breakdown of how students did on real past exam questions.

ResultsPlus
Examiner's Tip

Make sure the angles add up to 360°.

This gives exam advice, useful checks, and methods to remember key facts.

ResultsPlus in the **ActiveTeach** provides interactive practice for AO2 and AO3 questions…

… and multiple-choice quizzes for each chapter to reinforce learning

1 COLLECTING AND RECORDING DATA

A school canteen wishes to introduce a range of healthy food options. It has a list of possible dishes that could be included on the menu. How could it find out which dishes students would prefer to eat? How could the students' choices be recorded?

◉ Objectives

In this chapter you will:

- consider the various stages of the statistical problem solving process, including how to collect, classify and interpret data
- learn how to collect and record data
- learn how samples are used and identify bias
- design and use tables of data.

◈ Before you start

You need to:

- know the addition number bonds to $9 + 9$
- know your multiplication tables up to 10×10
- understand decimal places
- be able to do simple arithmetic in your head
- be able to carry out simple measurements using rulers and weighing scales.

1.1 Introduction to data

Objectives

- You can understand the stages of an investigation.
- You understand place value and can multiply and divide any numbers by powers of 10.
- You can classify data as qualitative or quantitative.
- You can classify quantitative data as discrete or continuous.

Why do this?

Companies need to collect and use data for a variety of reasons. For example, a crisp manufacturer might want to find out which flavours people prefer.

Get Ready

How can you find the following information?

a The average amount of dinner money for classmates.
b What flights there were from Manchester to Washington D.C.
c How many people voted for the Green Party in the last election.

Handling data cycle

Key Points

- **Statistics** is an area of mathematics concerned with collecting and **interpreting** information.
- The statistical investigation process will usually involve a number of stages:
  - specifying the problem
  - deciding what information to collect
  - collecting the information
  - presenting and displaying the information
  - interpreting the findings
  - drawing **conclusions**.

Specify the problem and decide what information to collect → Collect the information → Present and display the information → Interpret the findings and draw conclusions →

Number

Key Points

- In statistics, information is called **data.** Data will often be numerical. Either:
  - a measure such as length, weight, etc. or,
  - the number of times (**frequency**) that particular type of data appears.
- In any number each digit has a different value, as shown in this table.

Thousands	Hundreds	Tens	Units		Tenths	Hundredths
4	2	5	6	•	3	8

In decimals the decimal point separates the whole number from the part that is less than 1.
This number is four thousand, two hundred and fifty six, and three tenths and eight hundredths.

Multiplying and dividing decimals by powers of ten (10, 100, 1000, etc.)

Key Points

- To multiply by a **power** of ten move the decimal point to the right by the number of 0s.
- To divide by a power of ten move the decimal point to the left by the number of 0s.

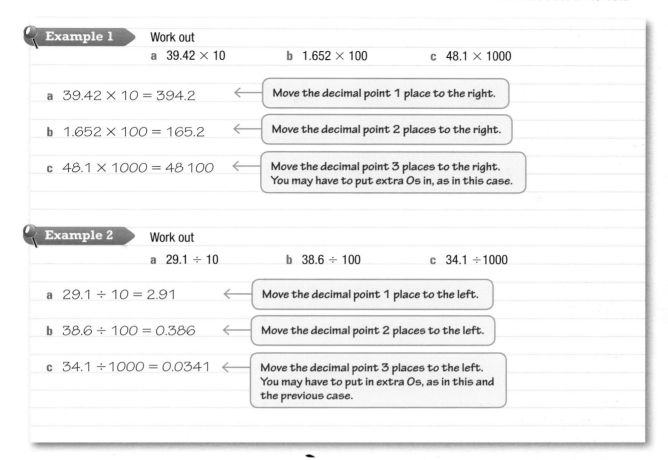

Example 1 Work out

    a 39.42×10 **b** 1.652×100 **c** 48.1×1000

a $39.42 \times 10 = 394.2$ ← Move the decimal point 1 place to the right.

b $1.652 \times 100 = 165.2$ ← Move the decimal point 2 places to the right.

c $48.1 \times 1000 = 48\,100$ ← Move the decimal point 3 places to the right. You may have to put extra 0s in, as in this case.

Example 2 Work out

    a $29.1 \div 10$ **b** $38.6 \div 100$ **c** $34.1 \div 1000$

a $29.1 \div 10 = 2.91$ ← Move the decimal point 1 place to the left.

b $38.6 \div 100 = 0.386$ ← Move the decimal point 2 places to the left.

c $34.1 \div 1000 = 0.0341$ ← Move the decimal point 3 places to the left. You may have to put in extra 0s, as in this and the previous case.

Classifying data

 **Key Points**

The **table** below shows some information about NHL ice-hockey players in the 2008–09 season.

Name	Shirt number	Team	Points scored	Age	Height (m)	Weight (kg)
Evengi Malkin	71	Pittsburgh Penguins	113	22	1.91	88.5
Alex Ovechkin	8	Washington Capitals	110	23	1.88	99.8
Sidney Crosby	87	Pittsburgh Penguins	103	21	1.80	90.7
Pavel Datsyuk	13	Detroit Red Wings	97	31	1.80	88.0
Zach Parise	9	New Jersey Devils	94	25	1.80	86.2
Ilya Kovalchuk	17	Atlanta Thrashers	91	26	1.85	104.3
Ryan Getzlaf	15	Anaheim Ducks	91	24	1.93	100.2

- **Qualitative** data is given in words such as the team name.
- **Quantitative** data is given as a numerical **value** such as height.
- **Discrete** data can only be a whole number, for example the shirt number.
- **Continuous** data can take any value, for example height.

> **Example 3**
>
> The following data has been taken from a survey of Year 11 pupils.
> Decide whether each one is qualitative, discrete or continuous data.
>
> | | |
> |---|---|
> | a Method of travel to school | b Number of brothers and sisters |
> | c Height | d Gender |
> | e Weight | |

a Method of travel to school can be described in words so it is qualitative.
b Number of brothers and sisters can only take certain numerical values so it is discrete.
c Height is a number and can take any value so it is continuous.
d Gender can be described in words so it is qualitative.
e Weight is a number and can take any value so it is continuous.

Exercise 1A

Questions in this chapter are targeted at the grades indicated.

G

1   Marcus knows that he needs 1.5 metres of wood to make a bird box.
Work out how many metres he needs to make 10 bird boxes.

2   A company orders a roll of material. It is 85 metres long.
The foreman wants to cut it into 100 equal size pieces. How long will each piece be?

A03   3   A garage forecourt fuel tank holds 25 000 litres of petrol. The fuel tank of a certain make of small lorry holds 100 litres of petrol. How many empty lorries can be filled from the garage fuel tank?

F

4   List the stages in a statistical investigation.

5   An estate agent collects the following four pieces of information about houses for sale:

Type of house   Number of bedrooms   Garden size   Price

a Which of these is qualitative data?   b Which is continuous data?
c Which is discrete data?

A03   6   James wants to find out how much time boys spend watching television compared to the amount of time girls spend watching television.
a Write down two pieces of information that James would need to collect.
b Describe the type of data James would need to collect.

1.2 Collecting data

◉ Objectives

- You can interpret scales on a range of measuring instruments.
- You can choose appropriate units for carrying out measurements.
- You can use 12-hour and 24-hour clocks.
- You can collect data by observation.
- You can design and use data collection sheets.
- You can understand and use a tally.
- You can group data into class intervals of equal width.

⊘ Why do this?

People collect data in different ways. For example, a sales assistant might use observation to record what items customers purchase.

⬖ Get Ready

What are the numbers given by each set of tally marks?
a ||| b |||||| c ||||||||||

Metric units

> **Key Points**

◉ Continuous data is often collected in metric units.

Measurement	Length	Area	Weight	Capacity/Volume
Basic unit	metre (m)	square metre (m²)	gram (g)	litre (l)

The word for each basic unit can be changed into a bigger or smaller unit by adding one of the following prefixes to the front of it.

Word	milli	centi		kilo
Meaning	$\frac{1}{1000}$	$\frac{1}{100}$	1	1000
Example	millimetre $= \frac{1}{1000}$ metre	centimetre $= \frac{1}{100}$ metre	metre	kilometre $= 1000$ metres

◉ To change between metric units you only need to multiply or divide by 10, 100 or 1000.

◉ To change from smaller units to larger ones you divide.

◉ To change from larger units to smaller units you multiply.
For example, to convert lengths

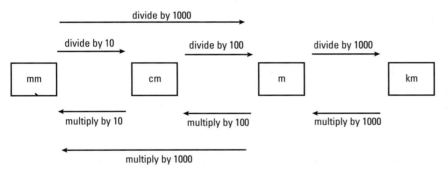

◉ When measuring an object, select an appropriate unit of measure.
For example, use metres for the length of your classroom, grams for the weight of a pen, and litres for the amount of water in a bucket.

Reading scales

> **Key Points**

◉ To collect data you may have to use measuring instruments.
You must be able to read different scales on measuring instruments.

◉ All scales have divisions marked on them and in most cases subdivisions too.
The scale below is a ruler.

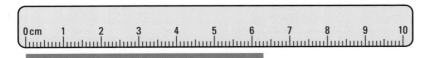

The ruler has cm divisions, each of which is divided into ten 1 mm divisions.
If an article being measured is 6 cm and 3 mm long, since 6 cm $=$ 60 mm, the article is 63 mm long.

◉ Most other scales are the same as the scale on the ruler. Here are a couple of examples.

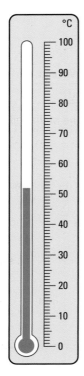

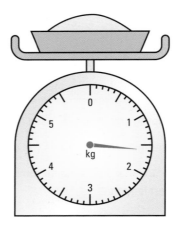

This thermometer shows a temperature of 52°C.

These scales show a weight of 1.6 kg.

Time

◖ **Key Points** ▶

◉ Clocks have two scales. One shows hours and the other shows minutes.

◉ A clock shows 12 hours, starting from the vertical, and 60 minutes.

◉ There are 24 hours in a day. The 12-hour clock does not tell you if it is morning or afternoon. To tell the difference we use am for times before noon (midday) and pm for times after noon.

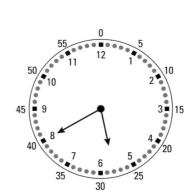

◉ Many digital clocks are 24-hour clocks. The 24-hour clock shows a day from 00 to 24 hours.

◉ The 24-hour clock times always have four figures.

◉ Here are some examples of 12- and the corresponding 24-hour clock times.

Times	12 hour clock	24 hour clock
2 hours past midnight	2 am	02:00
Half past 10 in the morning	10.30 am	10:30
10 past three in the afternoon	3.10 pm	15:10
Quarter past 7 in the evening	7.15 pm	19:15

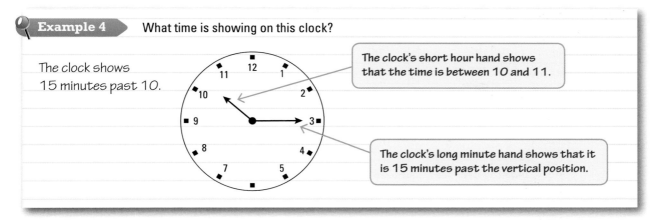

Example 4   What time is showing on this clock?

The clock shows 15 minutes past 10.

The clock's short hour hand shows that the time is between 10 and 11.

The clock's long minute hand shows that it is 15 minutes past the vertical position.

Collecting data

Key Points

- One way of collecting data is by **observation**: if you want to find out which types of vehicles travelled along a particular road, you could stand outside, observe and collect this information.

- A **data collection sheet** is used when **collecting data by observation**. The diagram shows a data sheet for recording the numbers of people who bought different vegetables at a supermarket.

Vegetable	Tally	Frequency
Beans	ЖⅠ ⅠⅠⅠ	8
Cabbage	ЖⅠ ЖⅠ ⅠⅠ	12
Carrots	ЖⅠ ⅠⅠⅠⅠ	9
Cauliflower	ЖⅠ	5
Onion	ЖⅠ ЖⅠ	10
Potato	ЖⅠ ЖⅠ ЖⅠ Ⅰ	16

- A **tally mark** is put next to beans each time a person buys them.
- The total number of people who bought beans is known as the frequency.
- The marks are grouped into fives with the fifth tally mark drawn through the other four.
- Putting tally marks in fives makes totalling up easier.

- If data is numerical, and widely spread, you can put it into groups of equal width known as **class intervals**. For example, class intervals for continuous data such as height will be of the form:
  $150 \leqslant h < 160$ This means the **variable** h is greater than or equal to 150 but less than 160.
  or $160 < h \leqslant 170$ This means the variable h is greater than 160 but less than or equal to 170.

- **Experiment**: if you wish to find out whether a coin lands an equal number of times on heads or tails, you could flip a coin a number of times and record the results.

- **Data logging**: if you want to monitor the temperature in a greenhouse, you could set up equipment to take temperature readings at set time **intervals**.

Example 5   The tally chart below shows the types of houses in which pupils in Class 10W live.

a Fill in the frequency column.
b Write down the type of house in which most of the pupils live.
c Work out how many pupils there are in Class 10W.

Type of house	Tally	Frequency
Detached	ЖⅠ ЖⅠ	
Semi-detached	ЖⅠ ЖⅠ ⅠⅠⅠ	
Terraced	ЖⅠ Ⅰ	

a

Type of house	Tally	Frequency
Detached	卌 卌	10
Semi-detached	卌 卌 |||	13
Terraced	卌		6

> Just add together the tallies $5 + 5 + 3 = 13$.

b Semi-detached ← Find the Type with the highest frequency.

c 29 ← Add together the frequencies $10 + 13 + 6 = 29$.

Example 6

The examination marks for 30 students are shown below.
Draw and fill in a data collection sheet to show this information.

40	46	35	27	35	18
22	35	48	24	12	18
40	41	32	39	25	15
26	44	33	16	40	45
12	32	23	43	34	19

Mark	Tally	Frequency
11–20	卌 ||	7
21–30	卌		6
31–40	卌 卌		11
41–50	卌		6

> The marks have been grouped together into four equal groups. The first group includes all the numbers between 11 and 20 inclusive. The groups do not overlap.

Exercise 1B

G

1 A car showroom has 30 cars. The colour of each car is shown below.

silver	white	blue	silver	black	red	red	black	silver	blue
silver	red	blue	black	red	silver	silver	red	black	blue
blue	silver	red	silver	red	red	silver	silver	silver	red

a Copy and complete the frequency table to show the colours of the cars.

Colour	Tally	Frequency
Silver		
White		
Blue		
Black		
Red		
Total		

b Write down the most popular colour.

2 A junior chess club has 30 members. Their ages are shown below.

14	15	16	13	14	16	13	14	16	16
13	14	16	16	15	15	14	15	13	14
15	15	15	14	15	16	16	16	16	15

a Copy and complete the frequency table to show the members' ages.

Age (years)	Tally	Frequency
13		
14		
15		
16		
Total		

b Write down the number of members that are 14 years old or less.

3 Naseema is going to make fancy dress outfits for the three children in her family.
The table shows the length of material, in centimetres, that she needs for each outfit.

Child	Shabnam	Usman	Asifa
Length of material (cm)	36	57	45

a Work out how many centimetres of material Naseema needs altogether.

b Work out how many metres of material Naseema needs altogether.

4 Here is part of a railway timetable.

Molly wants to travel from Carnforth to Grange.
She wants to arrive before 4.15 pm.

a Which train should she catch?

Bradley says 'Good, this timetable shows that
there is a train that arrives in Ulverston at 7.30 pm.'

b Explain why Bradley is wrong.

Station	Train A	Train B	Train C
Lancaster	15:33	16:14	16:55
Carnforth	15:43	16:22	17:05
Arnside	15:54	16:32	17:16
Grange	16:00	16:38	17:22
Ulverston	16:17	16:54	17:30

A03

5 A scientist measured 24 worms. Their lengths, in centimetres, are shown below.

5	8	6	10	11	6
7	8	10	11	7	9
5	8	10	11	5	10
9	6	8	10	11	10

a Draw a table or chart to show the lengths of the worms.

b Write down the number of worms that are 5–6 centimetres long.

F

A02

6 It takes 110 g of flour to make a sponge cake.
Maria wants to make 10 sponge cakes for the village fete.
Maria has a 1 kg bag of flour.
Has she got enough flour to make the 10 sponge cakes? Explain your answer.

A03

F A02 A03

7 Lemonade is supplied in 1.5 litre bottles. A lemonade glass holds 75 ml.

a Work out how many glasses can be filled from a 1.5 litre bottle.

A bottle of lemonade costs £1.20 from a supermarket.

b How many bottles would be needed to fill 50 glasses?

c How much would this cost?

1.3 Questionnaires

◎ Objectives

● You can collect data using a questionnaire.
● You can criticise questions in a questionnaire.

❔ Why do this?

Many organisations use questionnaires to collect data. For example, a youth centre may use one to find out whether it is providing the type of facilities that young people want.

◈ Get Ready

Describe a good way to record data collected by observation.

🔍 Key Points

● A **questionnaire** is a list of questions designed to collect data. There are two types of question used on questionnaires.

　◉ An **open question** is one that has no suggested answers.

　◉ A **closed question** is one that has a set of answers to choose from. It is easier to summarise the data from this type of question.

● When designing a questionnaire, you need to make sure that possible answers are clear, do not overlap and cover all possibilities.

🔍 Example 7　Here is an example of part of a well-designed questionnaire.

1. Tick one box to indicate your age group.

　□ Under 21　□ 21 to 30　□ 31 to 40　□ 41 to 50　□ Over 50

　← *These are response boxes. The categories do not overlap.*

2. How often have you visited the dentist in the last 4 years? Tick one box.

　□ Never　□ 1 or 2 times　□ 3 or 4 times　□ 5 or 6 times　□ More than 6 times

　← *This allows for other answers.*

3. Do you agree or disagree that people who visit a dentist regularly have fewer fillings in their teeth?

　□ Agree　□ Disagree　← *'Agree' or 'Disagree' makes the question unbiased.*

Example 8   Here are the same questions but with a number of common errors.

1. Tick one box to indicate your age group.

    ☐   ☐   ☐   ☐
    Under 20   20 to 30   31 to 40   40 to 50

    > The categories overlap so 40-year-olds could tick two boxes.
    > Other answers are not allowed for. Where does a 60-year-old tick?

2. How often have you visited the dentist in the last 4 years? Tick one box.

    ☐   ☐   ☐   ☐   ☐
    Never   Seldom   Sometimes Often   Very often

    > It is difficult to decide what these words mean.

3. Do you agree that people who visit the dentist regularly have fewer fillings?

    ☐   ☐
    Agree   Disagree

    > By asking 'Do you agree...' you are inviting the answer 'Agree'. This is called a *biased* question.

Exercise 1C

1   Jenni is doing a survey on golf.
    She writes the following question for a questionnaire.
    'How often do you watch golf on TV each month?'

    ☐ 0–1 time   ☐ 1–2 times   ☐ 3–4 times

    Write down one reason why this is a poor question.

2   A market research company intends to put the following question on a questionnaire.
    'How old are you?'
    Write down one reason why this is a poor question.

3   A town council asks the following question in a survey about council offices.
    'Do you agree that the council should have new council offices?'

    ☐ Yes   ☐ Not sure

    Write down two reasons why this is a poor question.

E

1.4 **Sampling**

◎ Objectives

- ◎ You can collect information about a population by using a sample.
- ◎ You understand how different sample sizes may affect the reliability of conclusions drawn.
- ◎ You can identify possible sources of bias.

◈ Why do this?

Market research companies always try to survey a representative sample of the population in order to ensure the accuracy of their data.

◈ Get Ready

It takes 15 seconds to get an answer from one student.
How long should it take for you to ask everyone in your class?

Key Points

- Asking a select number of people their view is called taking a **sample**. It would be difficult to ask every person their view, so a sample is used to give information about the **population** as a whole.

- The sample must be unbiased.

- **Bias** occurs where:
  - the sample picked does not truly represent the population
  - the sample is too small.

- You need to make sure every member of the population has an equal **chance** of being picked. This is called **random sampling** and the sample will then not be biased.

- The size of a sample may vary. The larger the sample the more **representative** it is and the more accurate the information collected.

A02 A03

Example 9

A pollster wanted to find out who people would vote for in an election. He stopped the first 100 people he met in a shopping centre on a Saturday afternoon and asked them who they would vote for.
Explain what is wrong with this way of sampling.

This is biased because:
- Choosing the first 100 people is unlikely to give good representation of the population; for example, not all people shop in shopping centres.
- Sampling on a Saturday afternoon only may not include people who shop on other days.
- Choosing people who are shopping on Saturday afternoon may leave out people who watch or play sport at this time.

 Exercise 1D

F **A03**

1 A supermarket manager is conducting a survey to find out how far people travel to the supermarket.
She is going to ask a sample of shoppers.
She decides to ask the first 10 people who enter the shop one Saturday morning.
What is wrong with this sample?

2 A head teacher decides to conduct a survey to find out how students feel about school uniform.
He asks the students in Class 2X.
What is wrong with using these students as a sample?

E

*** 3** A magazine editor wants to find out people's views about the magazine.
He organises a poll where 30 people are telephoned and asked their opinions.
Give reasons why you think this would not give a true picture of people's views.

1.5 Two-way and other tables

Objectives

- You can design and use two-way tables.
- You can get data from lists and tables.
- You can round numbers to a given degree of accuracy.

Why do this?

Most organisations use databases to store and retrieve vital information.

Get Ready

Each row has the same total and each column has the same total. Work out the values of A and B.

4	9	8	3	16
2	9	A	11	B
18	6	4	10	2

Key Points

- A **two-way table** can be used to show how data falls into two different categories.

- For example, you may collect students' sex and whether they are right- or left-handed. The diagram below shows how you could record this in a two-way table.

This is the number of boys who are left-handed.

	Left-handed	Right-handed	Total
Boys	6	14	20
Girls	4	16	20
Total	10	30	40

This is the total number of children.

This is the total number of left-handed children.

This is the number of girls who are right-handed.

- If data has been collected by the person who is going to use it then it is called **primary data**.

- Data that has been collected by somebody else is known as **secondary data.** Secondary data is usually obtained from a **database.** This is data that has been collected and put together so that information can be quickly found.

Example 10

A teacher conducted a survey to find out what colour uniform students would prefer.
He gave students three possible colour choices.
The information below shows the results for girls and boys.

Girls

Green	Red	Green	Blue	Blue
Red	Green	Green	Red	Blue
Blue	Green	Red	Blue	Green
Green	Blue	Green	Green	Blue

Boys

Red	Red	Blue	Green	Blue
Blue	Blue	Green	Red	Red
Blue	Red	Blue	Red	Red
Green	Blue	Blue	Red	Red

a Display this information in a table.

b Write down the girls' top choice of colour.

c Write down the boys' top choice of colour.

d Write down the colour that was chosen by most of the students.

A02

a

	Red	Blue	Green	Total
Girls	4	7	9	20
Boys	9	8	3	20
Total	13	15	12	40

The most suitable table is a two-way table.
Count up the number of girls who chose red and enter it here.
Do the same for the other colours and the boys' colours.

Total the rows and columns.

b Green ← Look for the highest number in the girls' row.

c Red ← Look for the highest number in the boys' row.

d Blue ← Look for the colour that has the highest total.

Example 11 The following two-way table gives information about types of housing on a new housing estate.

	Detached	Semi-detached	Terraced	Total
2 bedrooms	4	4		16
3 bedrooms	3		4	
4 bedrooms		1	1	4
Total	9	8		30

a Complete the table.

b Which type of house was the most common on the estate?

c Which types of housing were the least common?

ResultsPlus
Examiner's Tip

a

	Detached	Semi-detached	Terraced	Total
2 bedrooms	4	4	8	16
3 bedrooms	3	3	4	10
4 bedrooms	2	1	1	4
Total	9	8	13	30

When completing a two-way table look for rows with only one number missing and fill these in first.
The numbers in each row must add up to the row total and the same goes for columns.

The total number of 2-bedroom terraced houses = 16 − 4 − 4 = 8
The total number of 4-bedroom detached houses = 4 − 1 − 1 = 2
The total number of 3-bedroom semi-detached houses = 8 − 4 − 1 = 3
The total number 3-bedroom houses = 3 + 3 + 4 = 10
The total number of terraced houses = 30 − 8 − 9 = 13

b 2-bedroom terraced houses

c There was one 4-bedroom semi-detached house and one 4-bedroom terraced house.

Exercise 1E

1 A teacher is working out a timetable for Class 10B. Of the 30 students:

seven want to do Art and Music

twelve want to do Drama and PE

five want to do Music and PE

six want to do Drama and Art.

Copy and complete the two-way table below to show these data.

	Music	Drama	Total
Art			
PE			
Total			30

2 The two-way table gives some information about the numbers of different ice cream cornets sold at an ice cream van in one hour.

	Large	Small	Total
Vanilla	8	10	
Chocolate	6	4	
Total			

Copy and complete the table.

3 The following two-way table gives information about the numbers of different types of membership at a small health club.

	Junior	Senior	Family	Total
Full week	14	36	24	
Weekends	28	56	20	
Total				

a Copy and complete the table.

b Write down the number of weekend junior members.

4 The two-way table below gives information about the meals chosen by people visiting a restaurant.

	Pizza	Salad	Pasta	Total
Gateau	12	10		25
Ice Cream	10		20	40
Fruit	4	2		
Total				72

a Copy and complete the table.

b Write down the number of people who chose pasta and ice cream.

c Write down the total number of people represented by the table.

Example 12 The database below contains information about past population figures, in millions, for the United Kingdom. It also shows predicted figures for later years.

	1981	1991	2001	2005	2011	2021
England	46.8	47.9	49.4	50.4	52.0	54.6
Wales	2.8	2.9	2.9	3.0	3.0	3.2
Scotland	5.1	5.1	5.1	5.1	5.1	5.1
N. Ireland	1.5	1.6	1.7	1.7	1.8	1.8

a Write down the population of England in 2005.

b Write down what the population of Wales is expected to be in 2021.

c What happened to the population of Scotland between 1981 and 2005?

d What is expected to happen to the population of Northern Ireland between 2005 and 2021?

a 50.4 million ← Read off the figure from the intersection of the England row and the 2005 column.

b 3.2 million ← This is the intersection of the Wales row and the 2021 column.

c It stayed at 5.1 million. ← Look along the Scotland row between 1981 and 2005.

d It is expected to increase from 1.7 to 1.8 million. ← Look at what the figure for Northern Ireland was in 2005 and then at what it is predicted to be in 2021.

Exercise 1F

G

1 The following table provides information about the weather in Aspatria.

	Maximum temperature (degrees C)	Minimum temperature (degrees C)	Sunshine (hours)	Rainfall (mm)
January	6.4	1.2	44.3	101.9
April	11.4	3.5	155.1	50.7
July	19.2	11.2	195.9	68.2
October	12.9	6.6	98.6	110.9

a Write down the amount of rainfall in April.

b Write down the minimum temperature in January.

c Write down the month that has the most rainfall.

2 The table below provides information about planets.

Name	Number of moons	Rings	Temperature (°C)	Day length (hours)
Mercury	0	No	167	4222.6
Venus	0	No	457	2802.0
Earth	1	No	15	24.0
Mars	2	No	−63	24.6
Jupiter	63	Yes	−110	9.9
Saturn	60	Yes	−140	10.7
Uranus	27	Yes	−195	17.2
Neptune	13	Yes	−200	16.1

a How many moons has Jupiter?

b Write down the temperature of Neptune.

c Write down the planet that has the longest day.

d Write down the planet that has the highest temperature.

e How many planets have rings?

3 The following table shows information about the distance and travelling times of major cities from London.

From London to:	Distance (miles)	Air (minutes)	Train (minutes)	Coach (minutes)
Edinburgh	393	90	250	520
Glasgow	402	90	270	480
Inverness	568	105	430	720
Newcastle	270	70	170	360
Birmingham	114	50	95	160
Manchester	184	60	120	250

a Write down how long it takes to fly from London to Edinburgh.

b Write down the place that is 270 miles from London.

c What journey takes the least time if travelling by train from London?

d What journey takes the longest if travelling from London by coach?

4 Here is some of the data Sarah collected on the lengths, in kilometres, of 5 journeys.

4.6   0.8   4.5   8.62   14.43

Round all these figures to the nearest whole kilometre.

5 Here is some of the data Nassim collected on the lengths, in centimetres, of 5 bolts.

1.63   0.86   2.54   1.62   3.45

The factory making the bolts needs to know the lengths to one decimal place.
Round all these figures to one decimal place.

G

F

E

6 The table gives some information about holidays in Malta.

Half board	3 nights		1 week		10 nights		2 weeks	
Months of holiday	**Adult**	**Child**	**Adult**	**Child**	**Adult**	**Child**	**Adult**	**Child**
October 2009	335	250	469	325	569	450	729	640
Nov/Dec 2009	225	180	315	250	385	300	499	360
January 2010	215	180	315	250	375	290	529	460

Mr and Mrs Balawi and their 10-year-old daughter Zana decide to go on one of these holidays. They wish to go for 10 nights in November.

A03

a Work out the total cost of the holiday.

b How could they have reduced the cost of their holiday?

Rounding numbers

Key Points

- If the number after the place you want to round to is 5 or more, you round up.
- If the number after the place you want to round to is less than 5, you round down.
- You can round to a power of 10, the nearest whole number or to a given number of decimal places.
- When rounding to the nearest whole number the measurement given will be inaccurate by up to half in either direction. For example, a reading given as 4 could be between 3.5 and up to 4.5.
- To round numbers to a given number of significant figures (s.f.), you count that number of digits from the first non-zero digit. If the next digit is 5 or more then you round up. If the next digit is 4 or less you round down.

Example 13

a Round 8736 correct to the nearest 1000.

b Round 8736 correct to the nearest 100.

c Round 8736 correct to the nearest 10.

a 8736 rounds to 9000 to the nearest 1000. ← The number after the thousands is 7, which is greater than 5, so you round up to 9000.

b 8736 rounds to 8700 to the nearest 100. ← The number after the hundreds is 3, which is less than 5, so you round down.

c 8736 rounds to 8740 to the nearest 10. ← The number after the tens is 6, which is greater than 5, so you round up.

Example 14

Round to the nearest whole number

a 4.55   b 4.28   b 4.5

a 4.55 rounds to 5 to the nearest whole number. ← The number after the decimal point is a 5, so you round up.

b 4.28 rounds to 4 to the nearest whole number. ← The number after the decimal point is a 2, which is less than 5, so you round down.

c 4.5 rounds to 5 to the nearest whole number. ← 4.5 is mid-way between 4 and 5. If a number is mid-way between two numbers it is rounded up.

Example 15

a Round 2.465 to one decimal place.

b Round 4.762 to 2 decimal places.

c Round 1.875 to 2 decimal places.

a 2.465 rounds to 2.5 to 1 decimal place. ← The number in the second decimal place is a 6, which is greater than 5, so round up.

b 4.762 rounds to 4.76 to 2 decimal places. ← The number in the third decimal place is a 2, which is less than 5, so round down.

c 1.875 rounds to 1.88 to 2 decimal places. ← The number in the third decimal place is a 5, so round up.

Example 16

Round 64.803 to

a 1 s.f.

b 2 s.f.

c 3 s.f.

a 60 ← The first non-zero digit is 6. The next digit is 4 so round down.

b 65 ← The second non-zero digit is 4. The next digit is 8 so round up.

c 64.8 ← The third non-zero digit is 8. The next digit is zero so it is already rounded.

Chapter review

- **Qualitative** data can be described in words.
- **Quantitative** data can be described using numerical values.
- **Discrete** data can only take certain numerical values.
- **Continuous** data can take any numerical value.
- When data is grouped the groups are known as **class intervals**.
- If **data** is numerical, and widely spread, you can group the data into class intervals of equal width.
- A **questionnaire** is a list of questions designed to collect data.
- An **open question** is one that has no suggested answers.
- A **closed question** is one that has a set of answers to choose from.
- A **sample** is part of a population that is used to give information about the **population** as a whole.
- A sample should be unbiased.
- **Bias** occurs where:
  - the sample picked does not truly represent the population
  - the sample is too small.
- A **two-way table** shows the frequency with which data falls into two different categories.
- **Primary data** is data collected by the person who is going to use it.
- **Secondary data** is data collected by somebody else.
- The data obtained from a **database** is secondary data.

Review exercise

G

1 Leanne asked each of her friends which one country they would most like to visit.
Here are her results.

USA	France	Italy	USA	France
Australia	USA	Spain	France	Italy
Italy	USA	France	Italy	USA
USA	Spain	USA	Spain	Italy

a Copy and complete the frequency table.

Country	Tally	Frequency
Australia		
France		
Italy		
Spain		
USA		

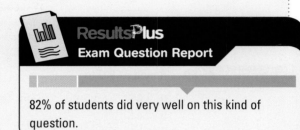

Results Plus
Exam Question Report

82% of students did very well on this kind of question.

b How many friends did Leanne ask?

June 2008

2 Tariq measured the lengths, in cm, of 18 books.
Here are his results.
14 13 16 15 14 14 17 13 14
16 14 15 15 17 13 15 14 16

a Complete the table to show Tariq's results.

Length (cm)	Tally	Frequency
13		
14		
15		
16		
17		

b Write down the number of books with a length of 16 cm.

March 2008

F

*3 James wants to find out how many text messages people send.
He asks 10 students in his class to complete his questionnaire.
He uses this question on his questionnaire.
'How many text messages do you send?'

1 to 10 ☐	11 to 20 ☐	21 to 30 ☐	more than 30 ☐

Write down what is wrong with this question.
Give reasons why this may not be a suitable sample.

March 2009 adapted

F

4 Nick has 6 coins.

Each coin comes from a different country.

Here is some information about these coins.

Coin	Country	Shape	Weight (g)
20 pence	United Kingdom	7-sided	5
500 yen	Japan	circular	7
10 centime	Switzerland	circular	3
1 dollar	Canada	11-sided	7
2 rupee	India	11-sided	6
5 cent	United States	circular	5

a Which coin comes from Switzerland?

b Which coin has the same weight as the 500 yen coin? *March 2009*

5 The table shows some information about six cars.

Make of car	Age (years)	Number of doors	Engine size (litres)
BMW	7	4	2.2
Ford	5	3	1.4
Mazda	8	4	1.8
Skoda	5	5	1.4
Rover	8	5	1.4
Volvo	9	2	2.4

One of these cars has an engine size of 2.4 litres.

a Write down the make of this car.

One of these cars is 8 years old and has 4 doors.

b Write down the make of this car. *Nov 2008*

6 Jason is collecting data about his school. He collects data about the following:

Number of school meals sold   Heights of the students

The colour of the walls in each classroom   Cost of school outings

Which of these is   i qualitative data   ii discrete data   iii continuous data?

7 Joe rolls a 6-sided dice and spins a 4-sided spinner.

The dice is labelled 1, 2, 3, 4, 5, 6.

The spinner is labelled 1, 2, 3, 4.

Joe adds the score on the dice and the score on the spinner to get the total score.

He records the possible total scores in a table.

a Copy and complete the table of possible total scores.

b Write down all the ways in which Joe can get a total score of 5.

One of them has been done for you: (1, 4).

c Write down all the ways Joe can get a total score of 8 or more.

+	1	2	3	4	5	6
1	2	3	4	5	6	7
2	3					
3	4					
4	5					

Nov 2007

E

* **8** Poppy wants to find out for how much time people use their computer.
She uses this question on a questionnaire and gives it to all the students in her class.

> **For how much time do you use your computer?**
>
> 0–1 hours ☐   3–4 hours ☐
>
> 1–2 hours ☐   4–5 hours ☐
>
> 2–3 hours ☐   5–6 hours ☐

Write down what is wrong with this question.
Is her sample biased? Explain why.

Nov 2008 adapted

* **9** Naomi wants to find out how often adults go to the cinema.
She uses this question on a questionnaire.

> **How many times do you go to the cinema?**
>
> ☐   ☐   ☐
>
> Not very often   Sometimes   A lot

Write down what is wrong with this question.
Use your answer to design a better question for her questionnaire.
You should include some response boxes.

Nov 2008 adapted

* **10** Valerie is the manager of a supermarket.
She wants to find out how often people shop at her supermarket.
She will use a questionnaire.
Design a suitable question for Valerie to use on her questionnaire.
You must include some response boxes.

June 2008

* **11** Yolande wants to collect information about the number of e-mails the students in her class send.
Design a suitable question she could use on a questionnaire.
You must include some response boxes.

March 2008

* **12** Melanie wants to find out how often people go to the cinema.
She gives a questionnaire to all the women leaving a cinema.
Her sample is biased.
Give two possible reasons why.

March 2008

* **13** Amberish is going to carry out a survey about zoo animals.
He decides to ask some people whether they prefer lions, tigers, elephants, monkeys
or giraffes.
Design a data collection sheet that he can use to carry out his survey.

March 2006

* 14 Angela asked 20 people in which country they spent their last holiday.
Here are their answers.

France	Spain	Italy	England
Spain	England	France	Spain
Italy	France	England	Spain
Spain	Italy	Spain	France
England	Spain	France	Italy

Design and complete a suitable data collection sheet that Angela could have used to show this information.

March 2004

15 The table shows some information about the cost, in £s, of all-inclusive holidays to Dubai.

Hotel	Economy Class		Business Class	
	3 nights	5 nights	3 nights	5 nights
Metro	469	595	1219	1345
Habtoor	505	655	1255	1405
Hilton	509	659	1259	1409
Atlantis	659	925	1469	1735

Wing and his wife plan to go to the Hotel Habtoor for 3 nights travelling Business Class.

a How much will Wing have to pay?

b How much could Wing save by travelling Economy Class?

A03

16 The table shows the distances (in miles) between some major cities in England.

Max is a travelling salesman.
He lives in Birmingham.
In one week he travels to Newcastle, to
Manchester and to Nottingham, before returning
home to Birmingham.
Work out how many miles Max travels to make
the journey the shortest.

A02

Birmingham					
109	Leeds				
90	72	Liverpool			
79	72	84	Manchester		
200	85	150	153	Newcastle	
50	137	36	97	153	Nottingham

17 A factory makes three sizes of bookcase.
The sizes are small, medium and large.
Each bookcase can be made from pine or oak or yew.
The two-way table shows some information about the number of bookcases the factory makes in one week.

	Small	Medium	Large	Total
Pine	7			23
Oak		16		34
Yew	3	8	2	13
Total	20		14	

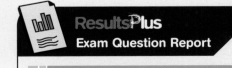

ResultsPlus
Exam Question Report

93% of students did very well on this kind of question.

Copy and complete the two-way table.

Nov 2008

E

D

D
A03

18 Kai lives in Manchester.

He has an hour-long interview for a job in Preston at 11:30

He will travel by train.

Here is part of the train timetable from Manchester to Lancaster and from Lancaster to Manchester.

Manchester to Lancaster			
Manchester	09:16	10:16	11:16
Bolton	09:33	10:33	11:33
Chorley	09:44	10:44	11:44
Preston	10:00	11:00	11:58
Lancaster	10:16	11:31	12:14

Lancaster to Manchester			
Lancaster	14:18	15:20	16:18
Preston	14:37	15:45	16:37
Chorley	14:56	15:56	16:56
Bolton	15:08	16:08	17:08
Manchester	15:27	16:27	17:27

It takes Kai 10 minutes to walk from his home to the station.

It takes 20 minutes for Kai to walk from the station to the place of his interview.

He wants to do some shopping near Preston station.

He needs to be home before 17:00.

Plan a schedule so that Kai gets as much time for shopping as possible.

	Time
Kai leaves home	
Train departs Manchester	
Train arrives Preston	
Kai arrives for interview	
Interview finished	
Train leaves Preston	
Train arrives Manchester	
Kai arrives home	

19 Ollie is standing in the school election, where all 240 students in the year vote for a student to join the school council.

He asks all the students in his class how they are going to vote.

a Why is this sample biased?

He then counts the first 30 votes and he has 10 votes.

b Estimate how many votes he will receive.

20 The Wildlife Trust are doing a survey into the number of field mice on a farm of size 240 acres.

They look at one field of size 6 acres.

In this field they count 35 field mice.

a Estimate how many field mice there are on the whole farm.

b Why might this be an unreliable estimate?

2 PROCESSING, REPRESENTING AND INTERPRETING DATA

Look at the bar chart of Bangladesh's annual rainfall. It has a typical tropical climate with three distinct seasons: summer, the rainy season and winter. It receives the majority of its annual rainfall during the rainy season (June to September). These rains flood fields and homes, leaving 70% of Bangladesh's land underwater. However, they also trigger the country's main crop, jute, to ripen. Farmers dive down to the roots to cut them and then leave the stalks to dry on higher ground.

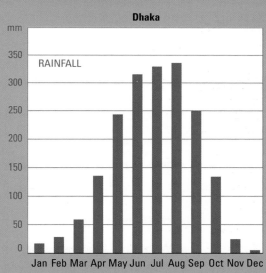

Dhaka

RAINFALL

Objectives

In this chapter you will:

- learn how to produce and interpret pictograms, pie charts and bar charts for various data types
- learn how to produce and interpret vertical line graphs for discrete data, comparative bar charts, composite bar charts, histograms for continuous data and frequency polygons.

Before you start

You need to know:

- how to add and subtract numbers to 360
- how to measure angles
- what a sector of a circle is.

2.1 Pictograms

⬆ Get Ready

Describe each of the following as either qualitative data, discrete quantitative data or continuous quantitative data.

1. Can be given as a whole number only
2. Can be described in words
3. Can take any numerical value

🌐 Key Points

- ◉ Data are often easier to understand if they are presented in the form of a diagram.
  When **representing** data the method chosen depends on the type of data.
- ◉ A **pictogram** can be used to represent qualitative data. It uses a number of symbols or pictures to represent a number of items.
- ◉ A **key** tells you the number of items represented by a single symbol or picture.

Example 1 The pictogram shows the colours of cars in a car showroom.

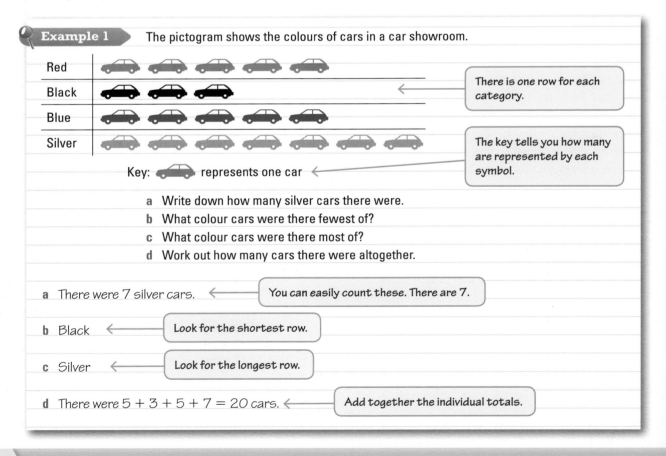

There is one row for each category.

The key tells you how many are represented by each symbol.

     a Write down how many silver cars there were.
     b What colour cars were there fewest of?
     c What colour cars were there most of?
     d Work out how many cars there were altogether.

a There were 7 silver cars. ← You can easily count these. There are 7.

b Black ← Look for the shortest row.

c Silver ← Look for the longest row.

d There were $5 + 3 + 5 + 7 = 20$ cars. ← Add together the individual totals.

Example 2

Atul asked some of his friends which sport they liked best.
The table shows the results.

Sport	Number of friends
Football	16
Rugby	6
Cricket	11
Swimming	8

Draw a pictogram to represent this information.
Use ⊕ to represent four friends.

Sport	Number of friends	Number of symbols
Football	16	$16 \div 4 = 4$
Rugby	6	$6 \div 4 = \frac{6}{4} = \frac{3}{2} = 1\frac{1}{2}$
Cricket	11	$11 \div 4 = \frac{11}{4} = 2\frac{3}{4}$
Swimming	8	$8 \div 4 = 2$

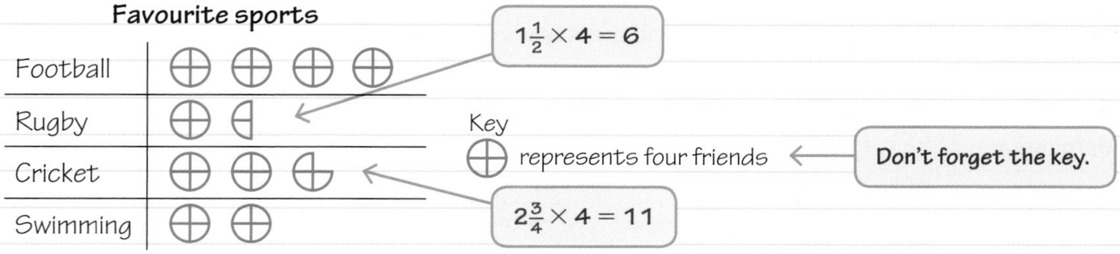

Favourite sports

Football	⊕ ⊕ ⊕ ⊕
Rugby	⊕ ◖
Cricket	⊕ ⊕ ◕
Swimming	⊕ ⊕

$1\frac{1}{2} \times 4 = 6$

Key
⊕ represents four friends

Don't forget the key.

$2\frac{3}{4} \times 4 = 11$

Exercise 2A

Questions in this chapter are targeted at the grades indicated.

G

1 The pictogram shows the number of emails sent from an office in one week.

Number of emails

Monday	✉ ✉ ✉ ✉
Tuesday	✉ ✉ ✉ ◗
Wednesday	✉ ✉ ✉ ✉ ▏
Thursday	✉ ✉ ✉ ✉ ✉
Friday	✉ ✉ ✉

Key
✉ represents
20 emails

a On which day were the greatest number of emails sent from the office?
b How many emails were sent from the office on Thursday?
c How many emails were sent from the office on Monday?
d How many emails were sent from the office on Tuesday?

2 The pictogram shows the number of drinks sold in one day from a machine.

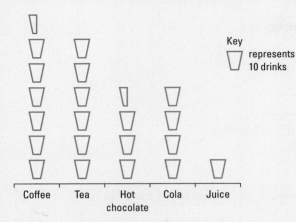

Key

⛛ represents 10 drinks

Coffee   Tea   Hot chocolate   Cola   Juice

a Write down the drink that was the least popular.
b How many drinks of tea were sold?
c How many drinks of hot chocolate were sold?
d Work out the total number of drinks sold.

3 The pictogram shows the numbers of three different types of pizza sold in one day.

Pizzas sold

Margherita	⊕ ⊕ ◿
BBQ chicken	⊕ ⊕ ⊕ ⊕
Hawaiian	⊕ ⊕ ◖
Meat feast	

Key

⊕ represents eight pizzas

20 meat feast pizzas were also sold.
a Copy and complete the pictogram.
b How many of each type of pizza were sold?

4 40 students were asked which of five subjects was their favourite.

Subject	Number of students
English	6
Mathematics	8
Spanish	4
Science	9
Technology	3

Represent this information in a suitable chart.

5 The table shows how 60 students travel to school.

Form of travel	Number of students
Walk	6
Bus	36
Train	2
Cycle	14
Car	2

Represent this information in a suitable chart.

2.2 Pie charts

Objectives

- You can use angle properties at a point.
- You can measure and draw angles to the nearest degree.
- You can represent the proportions of different categories of data using a pie chart.
- You can use pie charts to find the frequency for each category.
- You can find the total population from a pie chart.
- You can find the greatest and least values from a pie chart.

Why do this?

A pie chart would be a good way to display a company's market share, or a school could use one to show the relative popularity of GSCE or A level subjects.

Get Ready

1. A sector of a circle takes up $\frac{3}{4}$ of the circle. What is the angle of the sector?
2. A sector of a circle has an angle of 18°. What fraction of a circle does it take up?
3. A sector of a circle takes up 290°. What angle is taken up by the remainder of the circle?

Properties of angles

Key Points

- In a full turn there are 360°.

- In a quarter turn there are 90°. A right angle is often marked on a diagram with a small square.

- In a half turn there are 180°.

- In three quarters of a turn there are 270°.

- Angles a, b and c are known as angles at a point.
  If you add together angles a, b and c you get a full turn.
  There are 360° in a full turn.
  Angles at a point add up to 360°.

  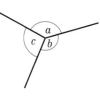

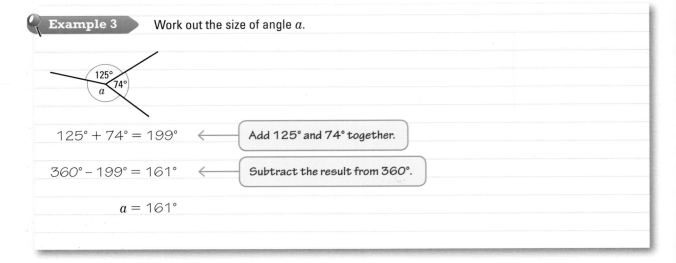

Example 3 ▸ Work out the size of angle a.

$$125° + 74° = 199° \quad \longleftarrow \quad \boxed{\text{Add } 125° \text{ and } 74° \text{ together.}}$$

$$360° - 199° = 161° \quad \longleftarrow \quad \boxed{\text{Subtract the result from } 360°.}$$

$$a = 161°$$

Pie charts

Key Points

⦿ A **pie chart** is a circle that is divided into sectors and shows how the total is split up between the different categories.

⦿ In a pie chart the area of the whole circle represents the total number of items.

⦿ The area of each sector represents the number of items in that category.

This pie chart shows people's favourite pets.

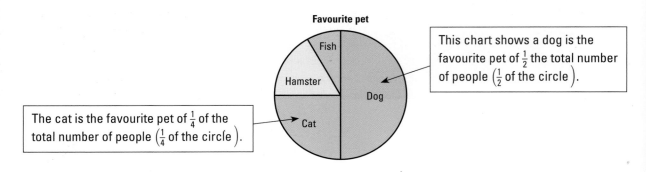

Favourite pet

This chart shows a dog is the favourite pet of $\frac{1}{2}$ the total number of people ($\frac{1}{2}$ of the circle).

The cat is the favourite pet of $\frac{1}{4}$ of the total number of people ($\frac{1}{4}$ of the circle).

⦿ The angles at the centre of a pie chart must add up to 360°.

⦿ The angle for a particular sector is found as follows:

$$\text{Sector angle} = \frac{\text{frequency} \times 360°}{\text{total frequency}}$$

⦿ To read frequencies from a pie chart use the formula:

$$\text{Frequency} = \frac{\text{sector angle} \times \text{total frequency}}{360°}$$

⦿ The frequency represented by corresponding sectors of two pie charts might have the same sector angle but the frequency they represent depends on the total frequency.

Example 4 The table shows the favourite colours of a sample of 30 students.

Colour	Blue	Red	Green	Black
Frequency	10	15	3	2

Draw a pie chart to represent this information.

Method 1

360 ÷ 30 = 12

12° represents 1 student.

> There are 360° in a full circle.
> There are 30 students.
> To work out the angle for
> 1 student divide 360 by 30.

Blue   10 × 12 = 120°

> If 1 student is represented by
> 12°, then 10 students will need
> 10 × 12° = 120°.

Red   15 × 12 = 180°
Green   3 × 12 = 36°
Black   2 × 12 = 24°

> The angle for each of the other
> colours is found by multiplying the
> frequency of the colour by 12°.

Results Plus
Examiner's Tip

Make sure the angles in a pie
chart add up to 360°.

Method 2

Blue $\frac{10}{30} \times 360° = 120°$

> 10 out of 30 students chose blue as their
> favourite colour so $\frac{10}{30}$ of the whole circle is
> needed to represent blue. $\frac{10}{30}$ of 360° = 120°.

Red $\frac{15}{30} \times 360° = 180°$

Green $\frac{3}{30} \times 360° = 36°$

Black $\frac{2}{30} \times 360° = 24°$

> The angles for the other colours
> can be found in the same way.

Draw a circle. Draw a line OA
from its centre to its
circumference.

Use your protractor to measure
the 120° angle.
Mark it and draw line OB.

Place your protractor on OB.
Measure the angle 180°.
Mark it and draw line OC.

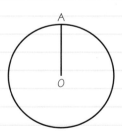

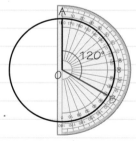

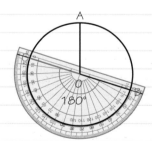

Continue in this way to draw 36° angle.
The finished pie chart looks like this:

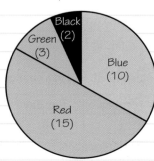

The frequencies have been
added to make it easy to
compare them.

Exercise 2B

1 Work out the size of angle b.

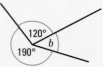

2 The big hand of a clock moves round from 3 to 6.
  a Write down the size of the angle it has gone through.

The hour hand of the clock moves through 120°.
  b Write down the number of hours that have passed.

* 3 40 passengers at a train station were asked which city they were travelling to.
The table shows this information.

City	Reading	Swindon	Bristol	Cardiff
Frequency	6	5	9	20

Work out the sector angle for each city. Draw an accurate pie chart to show this information.

* 4 Ryan asked 60 friends to name their favourite fruit. The table shows his results.

Fruit	Strawberry	Apple	Banana	Grape	Orange
Frequency	25	15	6	9	5

Work out the sector angle for each flavour. Draw an accurate pie chart to show this information.

* 5 The table shows the time it takes each of 30 people to travel to work.
Draw an accurate chart to show this information.

Time in minutes	Frequency
Less than 10	3
Between 10 and <15	4
Between 15 and 30	12
More than 30	11

* 6 The table shows information about the 540 books in a small library.

Category	Thriller	Classic	Romance	Non-fiction
Frequency	120	60	270	90

Draw an accurate chart to show this information.

* 7 The table shows the numbers of the different types of cars in a car park.

Type of car	Ford	Nissan	Toyota	Renault
Frequency	24	30	27	9

Draw an accurate pie chart to show this information.

* 8 The table shows the number of students absent in a year group on each of five days.

Day	Monday	Tuesday	Wednesday	Thursday	Friday
Number of students absent	7	8	10	6	5

Draw an accurate chart to show this information.

Example 5 The pie chart shows the numbers of each type of pet seen in a vet's surgery one morning.
There were 20 pets altogether.

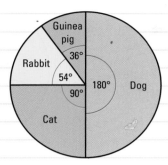

a Which type of pet was most common?

b Work out the number of each type of pet.

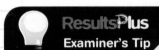

Examiner's Tip

In an exam 'work out' means calculate the frequency, so don't just measure the angle.

a Dog is the most common pet. | This has the largest sector. |

b **Method 1**

$$\text{Dog frequency} = \frac{\text{sector angle} \times \text{total frequency}}{360°}$$

$$= \frac{180° \times 20}{360°} = 10$$

$$\text{Cat frequency} = \frac{90° \times 20}{360°} = 5$$

$$\text{Rabbit frequency} = \frac{54° \times 20}{360°} = 3$$

$$\text{Guinea pig frequency} = \frac{36° \times 20}{360°} = 2$$

Examiner's Tip

Always add up the frequencies for each sector to make sure they total to the right number.

Method 2

If 20 pets are represented by 360°, then 1 pet is represented by $\frac{360}{20} = 18°$.
Divide each angle by 18°.

$$\text{Dog frequency} = \frac{180°}{18°} = 10 \qquad \text{Cat frequency} = \frac{90°}{18°} = 5$$

$$\text{Rabbit frequency} = \frac{54°}{18°} = 3 \qquad \text{Guinea pig frequency} = \frac{36°}{18°} = 2$$

Exercise 2C

E

1 120 adults were asked to name their favourite pastime.
   The pie chart shows the results of this survey.
   a Which was the most popular pastime?
   b Which pastime was the least popular?
   c What fraction of the adults say going out with friends is their
      favourite pastime? Give your fraction in its simplest form.
   d How many of the adults prefer going out with friends?

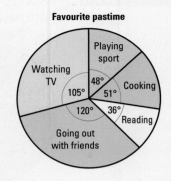
Favourite pastime

2 The pie chart shows the holiday destinations of 90 girls.
   a Which destination is the most popular?
   b How many degrees represent one person on the pie chart?
   c How many girls said Great Britain was their holiday destination?
   d What angle represents Greece on the pie chart?
   e How many girls said Greece was their holiday destination?

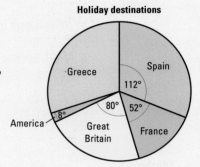
Holiday destinations

3 The pie chart shows information about how Letitia spends
   her time in one 24-hour day.
   Copy and complete the table. You will need to measure the
   angles in the pie chart.

Letitia's day

Activity	Angle (degrees)	Number of hours
Sleep		
School		
Play		
Watch TV		
Eat		
Homework		

4 The pie chart shows information about the makes of car driven by
   1200 people.
   a What fraction of the 1200 people drive a Nissan?
      Give your fraction in its simplest form.
   b How many people drive a Nissan?
   c How many people are represented by 1 degree in the pie chart?
   d How many people drive a Toyota?

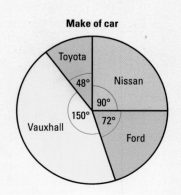
Make of car

5   In a survey, some adults were asked to name their favourite ice cream flavour. The results are shown in the pie chart.

30 adults said that mint was their favourite ice cream flavour.

a   How many degrees represent one person in the pie chart?

b   How many adults took part in the survey?

A corner shop wishes to stock 2 varieties of ice cream.

c   Suggest, with reasons, what they should stock.

Favourite ice cream

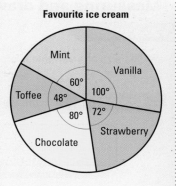

6   In a survey, some students were asked to name their favourite animal. The pie chart shows information about their answers.

a   Write down the fraction of the students who answered horse. Write your fraction in its simplest form.

12 students answered horse.

b   Work out the number of students that took part in the survey.

Favourite animal

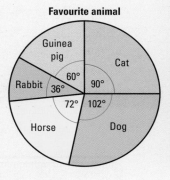

E

2.3 Bar charts

◎ Objectives

○ You can measure and draw lines to the nearest mm.

○ You can represent qualitative data as a bar chart.

○ You can represent grouped discrete data as a bar chart.

○ You can read off frequency values from a bar chart, and find the greatest and least values.

○ You can find total populations from a bar chart.

❓ Why do this?

It is easy to see data shown on a bar chart and read off individual values by using the heights of the bars. They can be used to show how many inches of snow fall per month or how many hours of sunshine you can expect per day in a certain destination.

⬆ Get Ready

Work out

1. $8 + 6 + 10 + 1$
2. $12 + 21 + 15 + 36$
3. 9×80
4. 35×4

Measuring and drawing lines to the nearest mm

Key Points

◉ The size of a variable is often represented by the length of a line or bar.

Example 6 Measure the length of the rod shown.

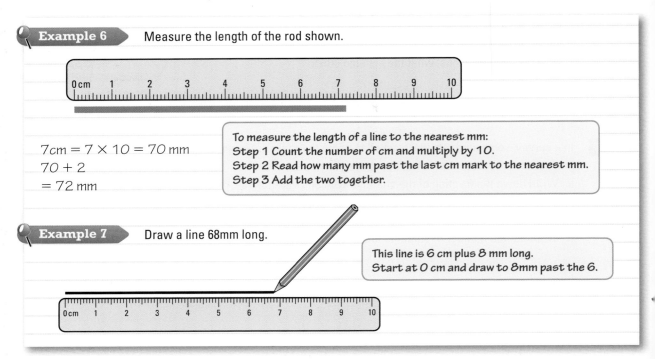

$7 cm = 7 \times 10 = 70 \, mm$
$70 + 2$
$= 72 \, mm$

To measure the length of a line to the nearest mm:
Step 1 Count the number of cm and multiply by 10.
Step 2 Read how many mm past the last cm mark to the nearest mm.
Step 3 Add the two together.

Example 7 Draw a line 68mm long.

This line is 6 cm plus 8 mm long.
Start at 0 cm and draw to 8mm past the 6.

Bar charts

Key Points

◉ A **bar chart** can be used to display qualitative data.

The **frequency table** shows the eye colours of 40 adults.

Eye colour	Brown	Hazel	Blue	Green
Frequency	15	8	12	5

The two bar charts also show this information.

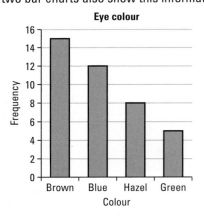

This is a vertical bar chart.

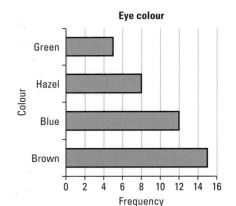

This is a horizontal bar chart.

◉ In a bar chart:
  ◉ all the bars are the same width   ◉ both the vertical and horizontal axes have labels
  ◉ there is a gap between the bars   ◉ the bars can be drawn horizontally or vertically.
◉ Bar charts may also be used for grouped discrete data.

Example 8 The bar chart shows the shoe sizes of a number of people.

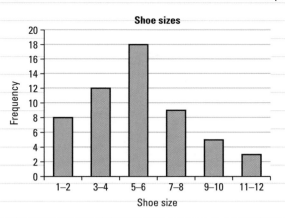

This bar chart shows, for grouped discrete data, how the total frequency is divided up between the groups. It shows the *frequency distribution* for shoe sizes.

a Which class interval has the greatest frequency?

b How many people wore size 3–4 shoes?

c How many people were there altogether?

a The class interval size 5–6 has the greatest frequency. ← Look for the highest bar.

b There were 12. ← Read off from the left-hand scale.

c There were 8 + 12 + 18 + 9 + 5 + 3 = 55 people altogether. ← Add the individual values.

Exercise 2D

1 Measure the line below to the nearest millimetre.

2 The bar chart shows information about the hair colour of all the students in a class.
   a How many students have black hair?
   b How many students are in the class?

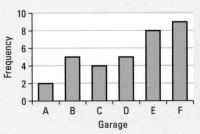

3 The bar chart shows the number of second-hand cars sold by different garages in one week in September.
   a Write down the number of cars sold by garage B.
   b Write down the garage at which most cars were sold.
   c Work out how many cars were sold altogether.

G

G

4   The bar chart shows the number of hours that some people spent watching television in one week.

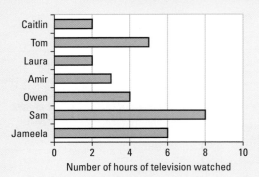

Number of hours of television watched

a   Who watched the most hours of television?
b   Write down the number of hours of television watched by Amir.
c   Write down the two people who watched the same number of hours of television.
d   Who watched 4 hours of television?

5   The table gives information about the meals served in a canteen.
Draw a vertical bar chart to show this information.

Meal	Fish and chips	Lasagne	Pie and chips	Cheese salad	Sausage and mash
Frequency	55	27	34	12	43

2.4 **Comparative and composite bar charts**

◎ Objectives

- You can draw comparative bar charts.
- You can draw composite bar charts.

❓ Why do this?

You might want to compare two people's results in different exams, or show the numbers of people employed in different industries in two countries.

◈ Get Ready

This picture shows three boxes stacked on top of each other.

a   Which box is the tallest?
b   Which box is the smallest?

◉ Key Points

- Comparative or **dual bar charts** can be drawn to compare data.
- In a comparative bar chart:
  - two (or more) bars are drawn side by side for each category
  - the bars can be horizontal or vertical
  - the heights of the bars can be compared category by category.
- A composite bar chart shows the size of individual categories split into their separate parts.

Example 9 The dual bar chart shows the number of houses sold by two agents in four months.

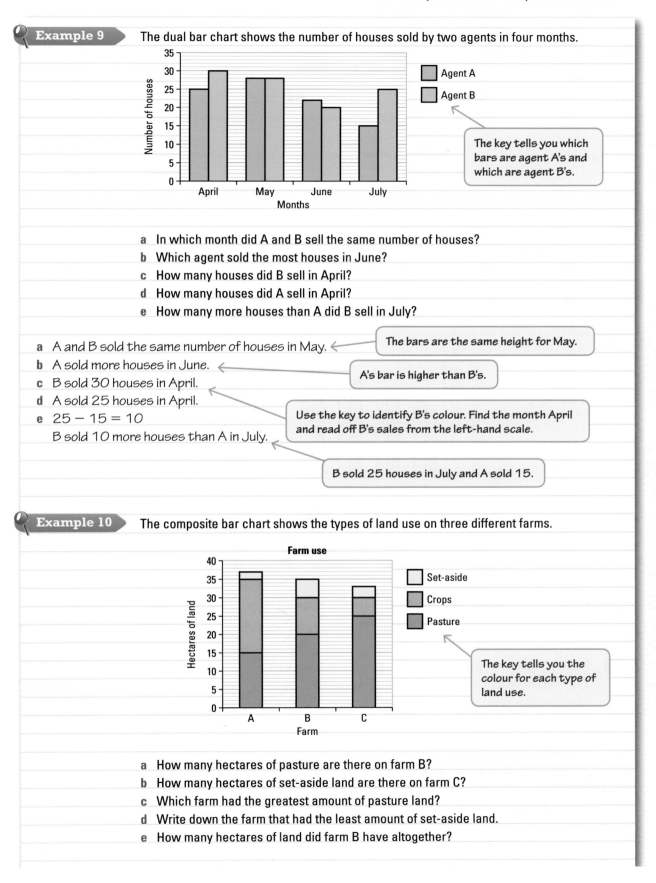

The key tells you which bars are agent A's and which are agent B's.

a In which month did A and B sell the same number of houses?

b Which agent sold the most houses in June?

c How many houses did B sell in April?

d How many houses did A sell in April?

e How many more houses than A did B sell in July?

a A and B sold the same number of houses in May.

The bars are the same height for May.

b A sold more houses in June.

A's bar is higher than B's.

c B sold 30 houses in April.

d A sold 25 houses in April.

Use the key to identify B's colour. Find the month April and read off B's sales from the left-hand scale.

e $25 - 15 = 10$

B sold 10 more houses than A in July.

B sold 25 houses in July and A sold 15.

Example 10 The composite bar chart shows the types of land use on three different farms.

The key tells you the colour for each type of land use.

a How many hectares of pasture are there on farm B?

b How many hectares of set-aside land are there on farm C?

c Which farm had the greatest amount of pasture land?

d Write down the farm that had the least amount of set-aside land.

e How many hectares of land did farm B have altogether?

a 20 hectares ← Identify the bar for farm B and use the colour key to find out which is pasture land. Read off from scale.

b 3 hectares

c Farm C ← The highest bar for pasture was farm C (25 hectares).

d Farm A ← The shortest bar for set-aside was farm A (2 hectares).

e 35 hectares ← Read off the total height of the bar for farm B.

Exercise 2E

1 The comparative bar chart shows the temperature in a number of resorts in April and October.

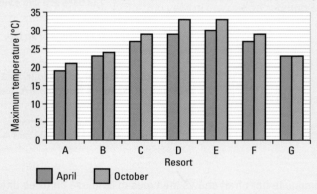

a Write down the maximum temperature in April.

b Write down the maximum temperature in October.

c Write down the resort that had the same maximum temperature in both months.

d Write down the resorts in which the maximum temperature in October was 29°C.

e Write down the resort in which the maximum temperature in April was 19°C.

2 Two factories making bolts employ male and female workers. The numbers of males and females are shown on the composite bar chart.

a Write down the factory that employed the most people.

b Write down the number of males employed in Factory A.

c Write down the number of people employed by Factory B.

d Work out how many people were employed by both factories altogether.

One factory has a bigger wage bill than the other.

e Which do you think this is and why?

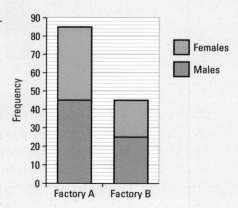

F

3 The composite bar chart gives information about the nutritional content of chocolate and shortbread biscuits.

a Write down the name of the biscuit that has the most carbohydrates.

b Which of the nutritional contents is the same in both biscuits?

c Work out the percentage of fat in a shortbread biscuit.

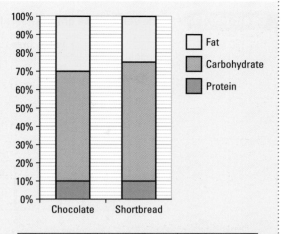

* **4** The table gives information about the numbers of males and females in each of the five classes in Year 11.

Draw a comparative bar chart to represent these data.

Class	Males	Females
P	14	13
Q	15	12
R	12	15
S	11	12
T	8	13

2.5 Line diagrams for discrete data and histograms for continuous data

Objectives

- You can represent discrete data using a vertical line graph.
- You can represent grouped continuous data as a histogram.

Why do this?

When quantitative data are shown as a line graph or histogram, it is easy to see and read off the individual values using the heights of the lines or bars, and to find the greatest and least values by comparing the heights of the bars.

Get Ready

This diagram shows five lines A, B, C, D and E.

a Which is the shortest line?

b Which is the longest line?

c Which two lines are the same length?

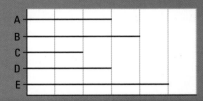

Key Points

- Quantitative data can be either discrete or continuous.
- A vertical **line graph** is used to display ungrouped discrete data.
- Because the data are numerical, the horizontal axis is a numerical scale.
- The discrete data can only take certain values on this scale.
- A **histogram** can be used to display grouped continuous data.
- A histogram is similar to a bar chart but, because it represents continuous data, no gap is left between the bars.

Example 11 The vertical line graph shows the number of children in a sample of families.

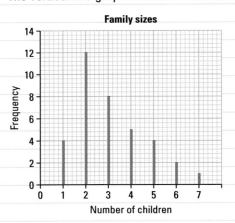

Family sizes

Lines are used instead of bars as the numbers of children can only take whole-number values. A bar would take up some more of the scale.
The chart shows the frequency distribution of the number of children.

a Which number of children had the greatest frequency?

b How many families had 4 children?

c What was the number of children that had the smallest frequency?

a 2 ← Look for the highest line.

b 5 ← Look for the line which comes up to 4.

c 7 ← Look for the lowest line and read off the value.

Example 12 The table shows some information about the number of minutes, m, taken to solve a puzzle by 50 people. Draw a histogram to show this information.

Time taken (m minutes)	$0 \leqslant m < 10$	$10 \leqslant m < 20$	$20 \leqslant m < 30$	$30 \leqslant m < 40$	$40 \leqslant m < 50$
Frequency	8	10	15	10	7

Because the data is continuous there will be no gaps between the bars.

For the class interval 0 to 10 the bar will be 8 high.

For the class interval 10 to 20 the bar will be 10 high.

For the class interval 20 to 30 the bar will be 15 high.

The greatest and least values can be seen easily from this histogram.

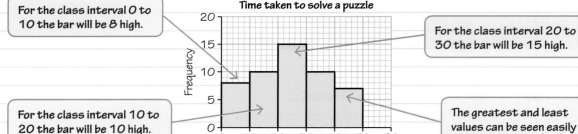

Time taken to solve a puzzle

Exercise 2F

G

1 The vertical line graph shows how often each number on a dice came up when it was thrown a number of times.

a How many times was the number 3 thrown?

b Which number was thrown five times?

c How many times was the dice thrown altogether?

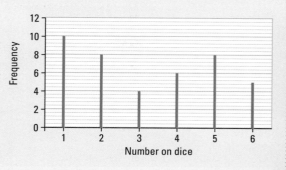

2 A survey was done to see the number of people travelling in each car entering a factory car park.

The results are shown on the vertical line graph.

a Write down the number of cars that had four people in them.

b Write down the most common number of people.

c Work out the total number of cars in the survey.

The factory wish to encourage car sharing.

They decide to ban all cars carrying less than 3 people from using the car park.

d How many people are going to have to change their travel arrangements?

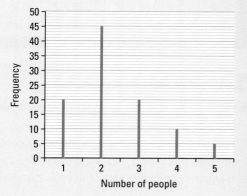

3 The histogram shows information about the times taken by some runners to run 100 m.

a Write down the reason why there are no gaps between the bars.

b Write down the number of runners that took between 12 and 14 seconds.

c Work out the number of runners that took more than 16 seconds.

d Work out how many runners there were altogether.

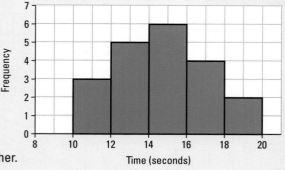

4 A speed monitor recorded the speed of cars travelling below a bridge on a motorway during a one-hour period. The table shows this information.

Speed (s mph)	Frequency
$20 \leqslant s < 30$	0
$30 \leqslant s < 40$	8
$40 \leqslant s < 50$	12
$50 \leqslant s < 60$	28
$60 \leqslant s < 70$	38
$70 \leqslant s < 80$	14

Draw a histogram to show these data.

2.6 Frequency polygons

Objectives

- You can draw frequency polygons.
- You can recognise simple trends from a frequency polygon.

Why do this?

In a sample of families, as the number of children in a family increases how does the frequency change? By drawing a frequency polygon the trend for the frequency to increase, decrease or stay the same can be recognised.

Get Ready

Draw a histogram for the following data.

Size	0 to <10	10 to <20	20 to <30	30 to <40
Frequency	5	10	8	6

Key Points

- When drawing a **frequency polygon** for discrete data, you draw straight lines to connect the tops of the lines on a vertical line chart.
- When drawing a frequency polygon for continuous data, you draw a histogram then mark the midpoints of the tops of the bars and join these with a straight line.
- Frequency polygons can be used to compare the **frequency distributions** of two (or more) sets of data.

Example 13   The table shows the number of children in a sample of families.

Number in family	1	2	3	4	5	6	7
Frequency	4	12	8	5	4	2	1

a Draw a frequency polygon for these data.
b Describe the trend of these data.

> You can draw a vertical line chart for the discrete data, and then join the tops of the lines to get the frequency polygon.

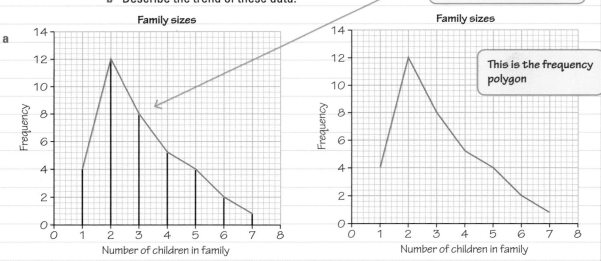

> This is the frequency polygon

b After an initial rise between families with 1 child and families with 2 children, the trend is for the frequency to decrease as the family size increases.

Example 14 > Draw a frequency polygon for the data in Example 12.

> This is the frequency polygon.

> You could also plot the midpoints and draw the polygon without the bars

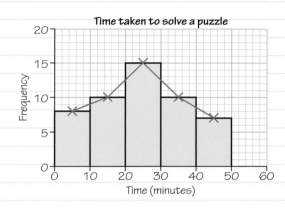

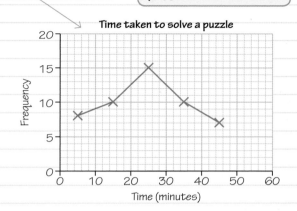

Example 15 > The two frequency polygons show the heights of a group of girls and the heights of a group of boys.
> Compare the heights of the two groups. Give reasons for your answers.

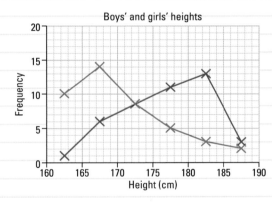

The boys are generally taller than the girls. ← The line showing the boys' heights is above the line showing the girls' heights to the right of the graph.

There were more boys above 172.5 cm in height. ← The lines cross at 172.5 cm and the boys' line is above the girls' line above this height.

There were more girls below 172.5 cm in height. ← The lines cross at 172.5 cm and the girls' line is above the boys' line below this height.

Exercise 2G

E

1 The table shows information about the shoe sizes of the members of a gym club.

Shoe size	Frequency
3	3
4	5
5	7
6	10
7	10
8	6
9	1

a Draw a vertical line graph for these data.

b Use your answer to part **a** to draw a frequency polygon for these data.

D

2 The table shows the distance the members of a sports centre threw a cricket ball in a competition.

Distance (d metres)	Frequency
$10 \leqslant d < 20$	2
$20 \leqslant d < 30$	6
$30 \leqslant d < 40$	15
$40 \leqslant d < 50$	20
$50 \leqslant d < 60$	4

a Draw a histogram for these data.

b Use your answer to part **a** to draw a frequency polygon for these data.

C

3 In three months Zainab travelled by train 20 times and by bus 20 times.
The frequency polygons show information about the amount of time Zainab spent waiting for the train and for the bus.

a How many times did Zainab wait for between 15 and 20 minutes for the bus?

b How many times did Zainab wait for between 5 and 10 minutes for the train?

c For what fraction of the times Zainab went by train did she wait for less than 10 minutes?
Give your fraction in its simplest form.

A03

d For which transport did Zainab generally have to wait the longest time, the train or the bus?
You must give a reason for your answer.

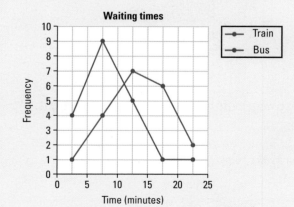

Chapter review

- A **pictogram** uses symbols or pictures to represent a number of items.
- A **key** tells you the number of items represented by a single symbol or picture.
- In a **pie chart** the area of the whole circle represents the total number of items.
- The area of each sector represents the number of items in that category.

$$\text{Sector angle} = \frac{\text{frequency} \times 360°}{\text{total frequency}} \qquad \text{Frequency} = \frac{\text{sector angle} \times \text{total frequency}}{360°}$$

- A **bar chart** can be used to display qualitative data.
- Bar charts may also be used for grouped discrete data.
- In a comparative bar chart two (or more) bars are drawn side by side for each category.
- A composite bar chart shows the size of individual categories split into their separate parts.
- A **line graph** is used to display ungrouped discrete data.
- A **histogram** can be used to display grouped continuous data.
- A histogram is similar to a bar chart but, because it represents continuous data, no gap is left between the bars.
- When drawing a **frequency polygon** for discrete data, you draw straight lines to join the tops of the lines on a vertical line chart.
- When drawing a frequency polygon for continuous data, you draw a histogram then mark the midpoints of the tops of the bars and join these with a straight line.
- Frequency polygons can be used to compare two (or more) sets of data.

Review exercise

1. Here is a pictogram.
   It shows the number of books read by Asad, by Betty, and by Chris.

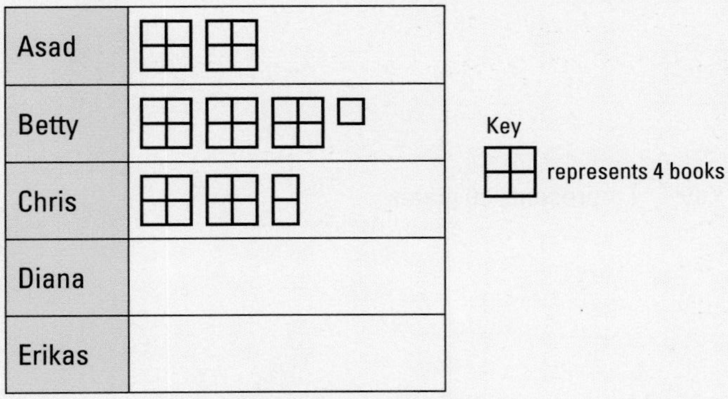

Key
represents 4 books

   a Write down the number of books read by
      i Asad   ii Chris.

   Diana read 12 books.
   Erikas read 9 books.
   b Show this information on a copy of the pictogram.

March 2009

G

G

2 The bar chart shows the number of TVs sold by a shop six days last week.

a How many TVs were sold on Friday?

b On which day was the **least** number of TVs sold?

c On which two days were the same number of TVs sold?

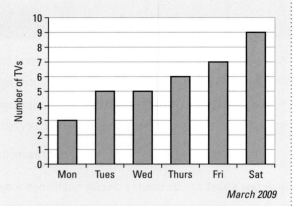

March 2009

3 Jessica asked some students to tell her their favourite pet.

She used the information to draw this bar chart.

a How many students said a rabbit?

b Which pet did most students say?

c Work out the number of students that Jessica asked.

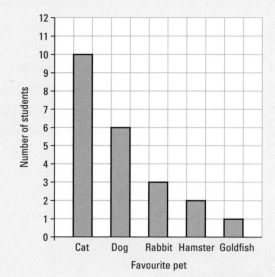

Nov 2008

4 The pictogram shows the number of plates sold by a shop on Monday, Tuesday, Wednesday and Thursday of one week.

Monday	◯ ◯
Tuesday	◯ ◗
Wednesday	◯ ◯ ◯
Thursday	◯
Friday	
Saturday	

Key: ◯ represents 10 plates

a Work out the number of plates sold on Monday.

b Work out the number of plates sold on Tuesday.

The shop sold 40 plates on Friday.
The shop sold 25 plates on Saturday.

c Use this information to complete the pictogram.

Nov 2008

5 Steve asked his friends to tell him their favourite colour. Here are his results.

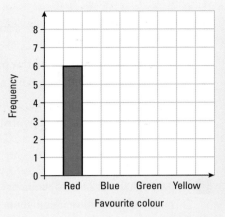

Favourite colour	Tally	Frequency
Red	‖‖	6
Blue	‖‖ ‖‖	8
Green	‖‖	5
Yellow	‖‖	3

a Copy and complete the bar chart to show his results.

b Which colour did most of his friends say?

May 2008

6 The bar chart shows information about the amount of time, in minutes, that Andrew and Karen spent watching television on four days last week.

Karen spent more time watching television than Andrew on two of these four days.

a Write down these two days.

b Work out the total amount of time Andrew spent watching television on these four days.

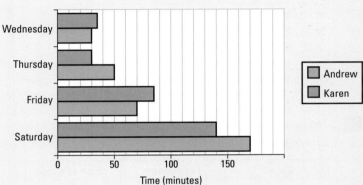

June 2008

7 Mr White recorded the number of students absent one week. The dual bar chart shows this information for the first four days.

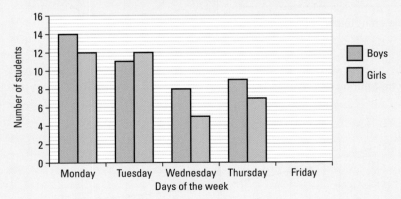

a How many boys were absent on Monday?

b How many girls were absent on Wednesday?

On Friday, 9 boys were absent and 6 girls were absent.

c Use this information to complete the bar chart.

On only one day more girls were absent than boys.

d Which day?

March 2008

E

8   Colin carried out a survey. He asked some students in
    Year 10 which type of film they liked best.
    He used the results to draw this pie chart.
    a   What fraction of the students said "Comedy"?

    20 students said "Horror".
    b   Work out the total number of students Colin asked.

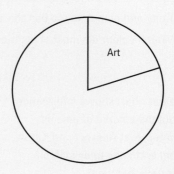

March 2009

A02 9   60 students were asked to choose one of four subjects.
        The table gives information about their choices.

Subject	Number of students	Angle
Art	12	72°
French	10	
History	20	
Music	18	

Copy and complete the pie chart to show this information.

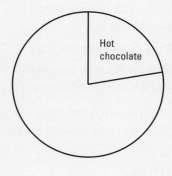

Nov 2008

10 The table gives information about the drinks sold in a
    café one day.

Drink	Frequency	Size of angle
Hot chocolate	20	80°
Soup	15	
Coffee	25	
Tea	30	

Copy and complete the pie chart to show this information.

Nov 2008

11 José is in hospital.
    Here is his temperature chart during one day.

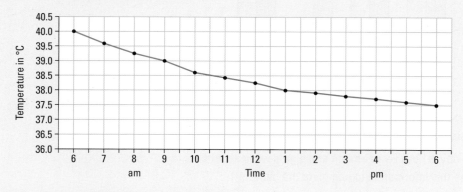

    a   At what time was José's temperature 39.0°C?
    b   What can you say about José's temperature from 6 am to 6 pm?

Nov 2007

12 The pie chart below shows government spending for 2008/09

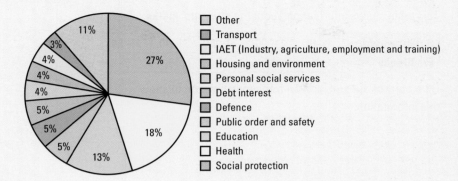

The government spent £21 billion on transport.

a How much did it spend on health?

b How much did it spend on public order and safety?

c What is the total amount of money that the government spent?

13 The table shows some information about the weights (w grams) of 60 apples.

Weight (w grams)	Frequency
$100 \leqslant w < 110$	5
$110 \leqslant w < 120$	9
$120 \leqslant w < 130$	14
$130 \leqslant w < 140$	24
$140 \leqslant w < 150$	8

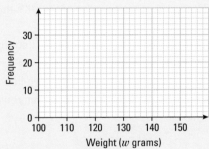

On a copy of the grid, draw a frequency polygon to show this information. *March 2009*

14 The pie chart gives information about the mathematics exam grades of some students.

a What fraction of the students got grade D?

8 of the students got grade C.

b i How many of the students got grade F?

ii How many students took the exam?

This accurate pie chart gives information about the English exam grades for a different set of students.

Sean says "More students got a grade D in English than in mathematics."

c Sean could be **wrong**. Explain why.

June 2008

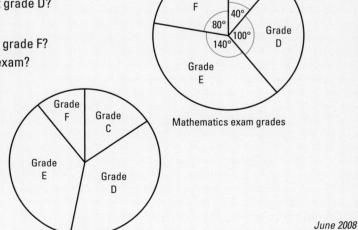

Mathematics exam grades

English exam grades

D

15 60 students take a science test.

The test is marked out of 50.

This table shows information about the students' marks.

Science mark	0–10	11–20	21–30	31–40	41–50
Frequency	4	13	17	19	7

On a copy of the grid, draw a frequency polygon to show this information.

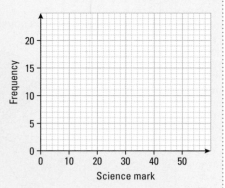

June 2008

A02 *16** The table below gives some information about the nutritional content of 120 g of baked beans.

Protein	Carbohydrate	Fibre	Other
6 g	16 g	5 g	

Copy and complete the table.

Draw a pie chart for these data.

17 The pie chart shows the sources of the UK's energy production in the early part of the 21st century.

Estimate the percentages of each type of energy and use your answers to draw a composite bar chart.

Draw a new composite bar chart showing how you think it will have changed by 2050, stating reasons for your answers.

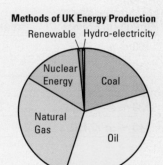

Methods of UK Energy Production

3 AVERAGES AND RANGE

The manager of a supermarket is asked to summarise the amount, in pounds, spent by shoppers at his supermarket. He wishes to give the average amount and an indication of how the actual amounts vary from this. What figures should he give and how can he calculate them?

◎ Objectives

In this chapter you will:
- use number operations on whole numbers and decimals with and without a calculator
- find the mean, mode and median of a set of data and discuss the advantages and disadvantages of these three measures of average
- find the range of a set of data
- use letters to represent numbers
- compare distributions
- use stem and leaf diagrams and frequency tables to find the mode, median and range of a set of data
- find the modal class and the interval containing the median of grouped data
- estimate the mean of grouped data.

◐ Before you start

You need to:
- know your multiplication tables up to 10×10
- understand decimal places
- understand frequency tables
- understand grouped data and grouped frequency tables.

3.1 Understanding and using numbers

◎ Objective

- You can add, subtract, multiply and divide any number.
- You understand and use number operations and the relationship between them, including inverse operations and the hierarchy of operations.

⑦ Why do this?

This will help you to solve problems and to calculate statistics such as the mean of a set of data.

⬆ Get Ready

Work out
a $27 + 45$
b $116 - 51$

Adding and subtracting decimals

🔍 Key Points

- When adding or subtracting numbers, keep the decimal points in a line.
- In whole numbers you have to imagine the decimal point after the last digit.

Example 1

Add together 3.42 and 5.18.

```
  3 . 4 2
+ 5 . 1 8
  8 . 6 0
```

Write the numbers under each other, making sure the decimal points line up.

Add the numbers (carried numbers are in red).

The decimal point in the answer goes under the other decimal points.

Example 2

Subtract 5.32 from 10.61.

```
  1 0 . 6 1
-   5 . 3 2
    5 . 2 9
```

Write the numbers under each other, making sure the decimal points line up.

Subtract the numbers.

The decimal point in the answer goes under the other decimal points.

Multiplying and dividing decimals

Key Points

● When multiplying decimals the number of decimal places in the answer is the sum of the numbers of decimal places in the numbers being multiplied.

● When dividing by a decimal number, continually multiply both numbers by 10 until the number you are dividing by is a whole number.

Example 3   Multiply 3.46 by 2.8.

$$
\begin{array}{r}
3\ 4\ 6 \\
\times \qquad 2\ 8 \\
\hline
2\,{}_3 7\,{}_4 6\ 8 \\
+ \quad 6\,{}_1 9\ 2\ 0 \\
\hline
{}_1 9\ .\ 6\ 8\ 8 \\
\end{array}
$$

> Write down the numbers, ignoring the decimal points. Multiply as for whole numbers.

> 3.46 has 2 decimal places and 2.8 has 1, so the answer has 2 + 1 = 3 decimal places.

Example 4   Divide 62.38 by 4.

$$
\begin{array}{r}
1\ 5\ .\ 5\ 9\ 5 \\
4\,\overline{)6\,{}^2 2\ .\ {}^2 3\ {}^3 8\ {}^2 0} \\
\end{array}
$$

> Divide as for whole numbers, ignoring the decimal point. If necessary add an extra zero.

> The decimal point in the answer goes over the decimal point of the number being divided.

Example 5   Divide 43.44 by 1.2.

$$43.44 \div 1.2 = 434.4 \div 12$$

$$
\begin{array}{r}
3\ 6\ .\ 2 \\
1\ 2\,\overline{)4\ 3\ 4\ .\ 4} \\
3\ 6 \\
\hline
7\ 4 \\
7\ 2 \\
\hline
2\ 4 \\
2\ 4 \\
\end{array}
$$

Order of operations

Key Points

- You use a set of rules to tell you the order in which operations are to be done.

  The rules can be remembered using the word **BIDMAS** which gives the order in which the operations are carried out.

  Brackets

  Indices

  Division

  Multiplication

  Addition

  Subtraction

Example 6   Work out $(4 + 3) \times 2^2$

$4 + 3 = 7,$	so $(4 + 3) \times 2^2 = 7 \times 2^2$	← Brackets first.
$2^2 = 4,$	so $(4 + 3) \times 2^2 = 7 \times 4$	← Indices next.
$7 \times 4 = 28,$	so $(4 + 3) \times 2^2 = 28$	← No Division, so Multiply next.

Example 7   Work out $3 \times 2^2 + (1 + 4)$

$(1 + 4) = 5,$ so $3 \times 2^2 + (1 + 4) = 3 \times 2^2 + 5$

$2^2 = 4,$ so $3 \times 2^2 + 5 = 3 \times 4 + 5$

$3 \times 4 = 12,$ so $3 \times 4 + 5 = 12 + 5 = 17$

Brackets first
Indices next
There is no Division, so Multiplication comes next, followed by Addition.
There is no Subtraction.

Exercise 3A

Questions in this chapter are targeted at the grades indicated.

Write down all the working for these questions. Do not use a calculator.

G

1. Joe works in a shop on Saturdays. He decides to work out how much money he takes in the first 10 minutes at work. He collects data from five customers.

   This is a list of the amount each spends.

   £1.34   £0.54   £1.00   £2.25   £0.37

   a   Work out how much Joe takes.

   b   In the till Joe has £6.70 in 1p coins. How many 1p coins does he have?

   c   If he changes the 1p coins into 10p coins, how many 10p coins will he have?

2   Emma has 4.50 metres of material. She needs 2.45 m to make a skirt.
    Work out how much material she will have left.

3   A factory owner gives out 18 questionnaires to each of the 8 sections of his workforce. How many questionnaires does he hand out?

4   Oliver finds £15.68 in an old box in his attic.
    He shares the money equally between his four children.
    Work out how much each one gets.

5   Write down the answers to the following.
    a 6^2 b 3^3 c $\sqrt{49}$ d $\sqrt[3]{64}$ e $2 + 2^2 - (6 - 3)$

6   Mark has been given the job of working out the cost of carpeting a set of rooms.

Room number	1	2	3
Length (m)	4	2.2	5.1
Width (m)	3	4	3.2

He records the data in a table.
The cost including fitting will be £10.50 per square metre.
Using the given data, work out the total cost of carpeting these three rooms.

3.2 Finding the mode, the median and the mean

Objectives

○ You can find the mode, the median and the mean of a set of data.

Why do this?

This will help you to understand detailed weather reports where they talk about average rainfall and hours of sunlight.

Get Ready

1. Write these numbers in order of size, smallest first.
    a 325   284   336   296   302
    b 0.6   0.59   0.55   0.625   0.61

2. The frequency table shows the number of times balls of different colours are picked from a bag.

Colour	Red	Yellow	Blue	Green
Frequency	6	10	8	14

    a How many times was a ball picked out?
    b Which ball was picked most?
    c How many more times was a blue ball picked than a red one?

Key Points

- We often describe a numerical data set by giving a single value that is representative of all the values in the set. We call this value an **average**. For example, we might say that 'The average height of members of a certain basketball team is 190 cm.'
- Three different averages are commonly used: the **mode**, the **median** and the **mean**.
- We may also be interested in how values are spread out. A common measure that is used is the **range**.

Finding the mode

Key Point

- The mode of a set of data is the value that occurs most frequently.

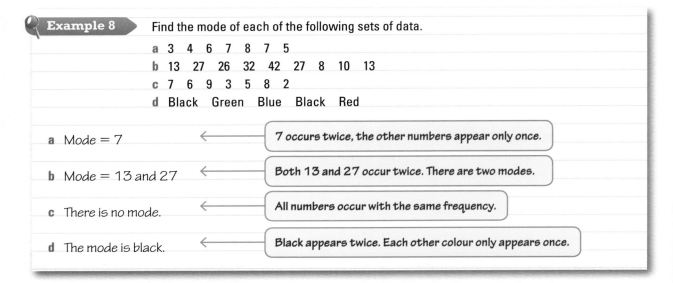

Example 8   Find the mode of each of the following sets of data.

a 3   4   6   7   8   7   5
b 13   27   26   32   42   27   8   10   13
c 7   6   9   3   5   8   2
d Black   Green   Blue   Black   Red

a Mode = 7   ←   *7 occurs twice, the other numbers appear only once.*

b Mode = 13 and 27   ←   *Both 13 and 27 occur twice. There are two modes.*

c There is no mode.   ←   *All numbers occur with the same frequency.*

d The mode is black.   ←   *Black appears twice. Each other colour only appears once.*

Exercise 3B

1   Find the mode for each of the following data sets.
   a 2   7   8   3   2   9   4   2
   b 10   12   14   10   15   12   11   18
   c 3   6   8   7   4   9   1   2
   d dog   cat   rabbit   dog   fish   mouse   dog

2   Briony did a spelling test every week for ten weeks. Her scores are given below.
   11   16   18   16   12   18   17   16   12   16
   Find the mode for these data.

3   Bo made a list of the colours of all the cars in a showroom. His list is shown below.
   blue   silver   white   red   red   black   silver   silver   green   silver   black
   Write down the mode for these data.

4   The hourly rates of pay for eight workers are listed below.
   £8.20   £8.50   £7.20   £8.80   £9.20   £7.20   £8.20   £9.90
   Write down the mode for these data.

Finding the median

Key Points

- The median is the middle value when the data are ordered from the smallest to the largest.
- If there are two middle values in a set of data, the median is halfway between them.

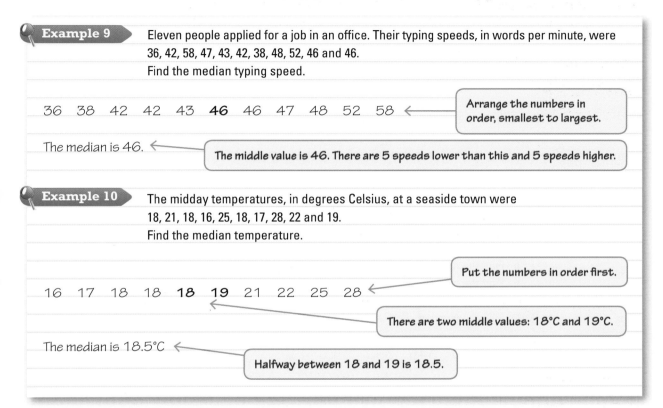

Example 9   Eleven people applied for a job in an office. Their typing speeds, in words per minute, were
36, 42, 58, 47, 43, 42, 38, 48, 52, 46 and 46.
Find the median typing speed.

36 38 42 42 43 **46** 46 47 48 52 58 ← Arrange the numbers in order, smallest to largest.

The median is 46. ← The middle value is 46. There are 5 speeds lower than this and 5 speeds higher.

Example 10   The midday temperatures, in degrees Celsius, at a seaside town were
18, 21, 18, 16, 25, 18, 17, 28, 22 and 19.
Find the median temperature.

Put the numbers in order first.

16 17 18 18 **18** **19** 21 22 25 28 ←

There are two middle values: 18°C and 19°C.

The median is 18.5°C ← Halfway between 18 and 19 is 18.5.

Exercise 3C

1   Find the median for the following data sets.

  a 2   3   3   4   5   6   7   8   8
  b 3   5   6   6   8   8   9   10
  c 5   5   6   7   7   8
  d 4   2   8   6   7   9   4   3   2
  e 2   5   6   3   7   8   1   9

2   The minimum night-time temperatures (in °C), in February, in seven towns are recorded below.
1.0   1.2   1.4   1.2   1.3   1.2   1.5
Find the median temperature.

3   The CO$_2$ emissions (in thousands of tonnes) for mopeds in Scotland over eight years are shown below.
38   38   39   41   44   40   41   39
Find the median CO$_2$ emissions.

4   The annual earnings of a group of six friends are shown below.
£20 500   £25 700   £30 900   £27 500   £22 000   £26 500
Work out the median earnings.

E

Calculating the mean

> **Key Point**
> ◉ The mean of a set of data is the sum of the values divided by the total number of observations.
> $$\text{mean} = \frac{\text{sum of the values}}{\text{number of values}}$$
> ◉ A short way of writing the mean uses the Greek letter sigma Σ to represent the sum of a set of values.

Example 11   Find the mean of the numbers 2, 4, 6, 6, 8, 9, 8 and 5.

$2 + 4 + 6 + 6 + 8 + 9 + 8 + 5 = 48$ ← Total up the values.

$\text{mean} = \dfrac{48}{8} = 6$ ← Divide by the number of values to get the mean.

Example 12   The weekly consumptions of electricity, in units, during an 8-week period were
340, 350, 340, 355, 340, 345, 340 and 450 units.

   a Find the mode.
   b Find the median.
   c Find the mean.

a The mode is 340 units   ← 340 occurs four times, each of the other values occurs once.

b 340 340 340 **340** **345** 350 355 450
                               There are two middle values: 340 and 345.

   The median is 342.5 units.   ← Halfway between is 342.5.

c The total of all values = 340 + 340 + 340 + 340 + 345 + 350
       + 355 + 450 = 2860   ← Find the total sum.

   $\text{mean} = \dfrac{2860}{8} = 357.5$ units   ← Divide by the total number.

ResultsPlus
Watch Out!

Some students use the term average – make sure you specify mean, mode or median.

Exercise 3D

1 Find the mean of the following data sets.
   a 3 5 5 6 8 9   **b** 2 5 4 7 5 3 8 6
   c 7 5 8 9 9 7

2 The number of school meals bought by 10 children in one week were
   2 4 3 5 5 4 2 5 5 5
   Work out the mean number of meals.

E

3 The heights, in centimetres, of 11 members of a cricket team were

172   174   190   190   185   186   182   189   190   185   192

a Find the mode.

b Work out the median height.

c Work out the mean height.

4 The numbers of emails received by a sample of six people during one week were

44   72   107   155   214   197

a Find the mode.

b Work out the median number of emails.

c Work out the mean number of emails.

E

3.3 Algebra

◎ Objectives

○ You can use notation and symbols correctly.
○ You can distinguish between the words 'equation', 'formula' and 'expression'.

⑦ Why do this?

By using letters to represent numbers you can write down general expressions and formulae that can be applied to a variety of situations.
You could, for example, write down a general formula for the mean of a set of numbers.

⬧ Get Ready

1. 3 apples + 2 apples = ____ apples
2. $a + a + a + a + a =$

Using letters to represent numbers

Key Points

◉ A letter can be used in place of a number.

Example 13 Paige gives a sweet to 4 of her friends and has one herself.
Work out how many sweets she has left.

She has $n - 4 - 1 = n - 5$ sweets left in the bag. ⟵ Let n = number of sweets.

 **Example 14** Paige buys 2 more bags of sweets each containing n sweets.
Work out how many sweets she now has.

The two bags will contain $2n$ sweets.
She now has $2n + n - 5$ sweets.
She has $3n - 5$ sweets.

Example 15 Rageh buys 4 cakes costing x pence each and a sandwich costing 86 pence.
Write down in terms of x how much Rageh spent.

Rageh spent $4x + 86$ pence.

Expressions, equations and formulae

Key Points

- $4x + 86$ is called an **algebraic expression**.
  An algebraic expression contains at least one letter.

- An **equation** also contains at least one letter but also contains an $=$ sign.
  $3x - 6 = 0$ is an equation.

- An equation can be solved to give a value for the unknown amount represented by the letter.
  If $3x - 6 = 0$ then $3x = 6$ and $x = 2$.

- A **formula** has at least two letters in it, and given a value for one of the letters the value of the other letter can be found.
  $y = 2x + 4$ is a formula.
  When $x = 1$, $y = 2 \times 1 + 4 = 2 + 4 = 6$
  When $x = 2$, $y = 2 \times 2 + 4 = 4 + 4 = 8$
  You could find a value of y for any given value of x.

Example 16 Write down whether each of these is an expression, an equation or a formula.
  a $4x + 6$
  b $x = 3y + c$
  c $x + 2 = 2x$

a This is an expression. ← | It has no equals sign. |

b This is a formula. ← | It has an equals sign and three letters. |

c This is an equation. ← | It has an equals sign and one letter. |

algebraic expression   equation   formula

F

Exercise 3E

1 Adam collects x pieces of data from each of his four friends.
   How many pieces of data does he have?

2 Mohammed has x 10p coins and y 20p coins.
   Write down an expression for the total amount of money he has.

E

3 Write down whether each of the following is an expression, a formula or an equation.
   a $3x + 7$ b $n + 6 = 8$ c $y = 2x + 6$

4 Mia earns n pence for every job she does. She does r jobs.
   Write down an expression for the total amount of money she earns.

5 Ellie collects data on the number of fish in each of 7 aquariums.
   10   12   10   9   5   14   10
   Work out the mean number of fish in each aquarium.

D

6 Luke buys 3 bunches of flowers costing x pounds each and a vase costing £4.50.

   a Write down in terms of x how much Luke spent.

   Grace buys 3 bunches of flowers costing y pounds each and a vase costing £3.00.
   Luke and Grace spend the same amount of money.

   b What can you conclude about the relative values of x and y?

3.4 Knowing the advantages and disadvantages of the three types of average

Objective

● You can discuss the advantages and disadvantages of different measures of average.

Why do this?

You need to be able to determine which type of average to use. For example, if you needed to find out the most popular football team, you would use the mode.

Get Ready

For the following data set find
a The mode
b The median
c The mean

   2   4   5   6   8   8   9

🔑 Key Points

⦿ The three types of averages are mode, median and mean.

Each of the averages is useful in different situations.

The table shows which measure of average to use.

Measure	Advantages	Disadvantages
MODE Use the mode when the data is non-numeric or when asked to choose the most popular item.	Extreme values (outliers) do not affect the mode. Can be used with categorical data.	There may be more than one mode. There may not be a mode, particularly if the data set is small.
MEDIAN Use the median to describe the middle of a set of data that does have an extreme value.	Not influenced by extreme values.	Not as popular as mean. Actual value may not exist.
MEAN Use the mean to describe the middle of a set of data that *does not* have an extreme value.	Most popular measure. Can be used for further calculations. Uses all the data.	Affected by extreme values.

Example 17 Shuabur recorded the number of spam emails he received every day for seven days.
Here are his results:

3   7   18   21   24   24   29

a   Find the mode, median and mean of these numbers.
b   Comment on the results.

a Mode = 24 ⟵ There are two 24 values.

Median = 21 ⟵ There are three values greater than 21 and three lower.

Total = 3 + 7 + 18 + 21 + 24 + 24 + 29 = 126 ⟵ Total the values and divide by the total sum.

$$\text{Mean} = \frac{126}{7} = 18$$

b   The mode of 24 has only one higher value.
This is because the number in the sample is small.
The mean has only two values that are less;
the two low values 3 and 7 have affected it.
The median is unaffected by the two low values.
The median is the best average to represent
these data.

Comment on how well the averages represent the numbers as a whole, and give reasons why they might not be representative.

✱ Exercise 3F

1 Jenny decides that she will use the mean to represent the following prices of jumpers.

£4   £5   £3   £7   £5   £42

Write down a reason why the mean is not a good average to use.

2 The prices of cars in a showroom were

£5750   £5750   £7750   £7550   £7950   £10 750   £11 550   £14 700

The garage manager puts up a poster saying 'AVERAGE PRICE £5750'.

  a Write down the name of the average he is using.

  b Is this a fair average to use? Give a reason for your answer.

3 Andy records the number of pieces of junk mail he receives each day for a week.

2   8   2   7   6   17   0

  a Find the mode.

  b Work out the median.

  c Work out the mean.

  d Comment on the values of these three averages.

*4 The following are the times, in minutes, it takes some people to travel to work.

10   10   13   16   17   13   40

Which average is the best to represent these data?

Give a reason for your choice.

3.5 Finding the range

◎ Objectives

- ○ You can calculate the range of a set of data.
- ○ You can compare data sets using a measure of average and a measure of range.

❔ Why do this?

If you were trying to negotiate a better rate of pay you might want to find the range of wages that your friends who had similar jobs earned, so that you could make sure you were getting a fair amount.

⬆ Get Ready

Write down the highest and lowest values in the following data sets.

a   2   7   4   3   5   13

b   22   25   26   19   24   29

c   150   161   152   130   145   156

🌐 Key Points

- ◉ The range of a set of data is the difference between the highest value and the lowest value. The range tells you how spread out the data are.

  range = highest value − lowest value
- ◉ The average and the range together give a description of the frequency distribution of the data.
- ◉ To compare the distributions of sets of data you need to give a measure of average and a measure of **spread**.

Chapter 3 Averages and range

Example 18 ▸ Here are the times, in minutes, that Fiona took going to school in the morning and
returning after school in the afternoon.
Going to school: 20, 18, 21, 17, 25, 28, 22, 23
Going home: 14, 17, 23, 28, 24, 12, 24, 32
 a Work out the range for each type of journey.
 b Which journey time was the most consistent? Give a reason for your answer.

a Range going to school = 28 − 17 = 11 minutes. ◂─── | Take the smallest value from the largest. |
Range going home = 32 − 12 = 20 minutes.
b The time taken to go to school was the most consistent.
The range was smaller. ◂─── | Don't forget to give a reason. |

Example 19 ▸ Samples were taken from two machines that filled jars of coffee. The weights of coffee, in
grams, were
Machine 1: 187, 192, 195, 198, 200, 200, 203, 205, 210, 210
Machine 2: 193, 194, 196, 199, 200, 200, 202, 204, 205, 207
 a Find the mean and range of the data for each machine.
 b Comment on these results.

a Machine 1

$$\text{Mean} = \frac{187 + 192 + 195 + 198 + 200 + 200 + 203 + 205 + 210 + 210}{10} = 200\,g$$

Range = 210 − 187 = 23 g ◂─── | Take the smallest value from the largest value. |

| The mean = $\frac{\text{total of values}}{\text{total frequency}}$ |

Machine 2

$$\text{Mean} = \frac{193 + 194 + 196 + 199 + 200 + 200 + 202 + 204 + 205 + 207}{10} = 200\,g$$

Range = 207 − 193 = 14 g

b Both machines filled the jars with the same mean amount of coffee.
Machine 2 had a smaller range. The weights of coffee were less spread out which shows the machine
was more consistent.

Exercise 3G

1 Find the range for each of the following sets of data.
 a 2 5 7 8 9 20 21
 b 3 7 3 5 7 14 5 13
 c 112 115 118 117 118 113

2   The scores in a game were

   12   14   11   17   23   25   22

   Petra says the range is 10. Is she correct?

   You must explain your answer.

3   The table gives the exam marks in economics and psychology for a group of students.

Student	A	B	C	D	E	F	G	H	I
Economics	72	70	63	87	83	56	88	44	65
Psychology	55	65	57	68	70	55	59	60	62

   a   Work out the range for each subject.

   b   Which subject had the most consistent marks? Give a reason for your answer.

4   Samples were taken from two machines filling bottles of mineral water.

   The amounts of water (ml) in the bottles were

   Machine 1:   30   29   30   30   29   32

   Machine 2:   30   29   29   34   30   28

   a   Find the range for each machine.

   b   Find the mean for each machine.

   c   Comment on your answers to parts a and b.

* 5   The heights of two teams of footballers (cm) were

   Max Rangers: 170   172   180   190   184   179   176   183   186   190   170

   Red United: 179   190   187   170   180   182   163   188   181   190   179

   Calculate the mean and range for each team and compare and contrast the frequency distributions of the heights of the two teams.

3.6 Using stem and leaf diagrams to find averages and range

Objectives

○ You can use a stem and leaf diagram to find the mode and median of a set of data.

○ You can use a stem and leaf diagram to find the range.

Why do this?

A stem and leaf diagram is a good way to put data into order.

Get Ready

Write these numbers in order of size, from smallest to largest.

1. 35   42   26   58   **2.** 152   151   154   153   **3.** 0.5   0.2   0.1   0.4   **4.** 0.1   0.11   0.12   0.9

Key Point

◉ A **stem and leaf diagram** makes it easy to find the mode, the median and range of a set of data.

Example 20

Here are the times, in minutes, taken by 12 people to complete a crossword puzzle.

35, 48, 42, 35, 38, 56, 34, 28, 52, 18, 43, 27

a Write these data as a stem and leaf diagram.

b Write down the mode of these data.

c Find the median of these data.

d Work out the range of these data.

a 18 28 27 35 35 38 34 48 42 43 56 52

Stem	Leaf			
1	8			
2	8	7		
3	5	5	8	4
4	8	2	3	
5	6	2		

> First write down the numbers whose tens digit is 1.
> Then write down those numbers whose tens digits are 2, 3, 4 and finally 5.
> The digit that each number begins with is called the stem.
> The following digit is called the leaf.

Key: 1|8 stands for 18 minutes

Stem	Leaf			
1	8			
2	7	8		
3	4	5	5	8
4	2	3	8	
5	2	6		

> Under stem write the numbers 1 to 5.
> Opposite each stem write the leaves.
> Don't worry about the order. This gives you an unordered stem and leaf diagram.

> Order the leaves to give an ordered stem and leaf diagram.

b The mode is 35 minutes.

> 35 appears twice, the other values only once.

c The median is $\dfrac{35 + 38}{2} = 36.5$ minutes.

> You can find the middle numbers by counting in from each end.

d The range is $56 - 18 = 38$ minutes.

> The largest and smallest values are the first leaf and the last leaf. The range is the difference between them.

Exercise 3H

D

1 Here is an unordered stem and leaf diagram.

0	1	6	3	4	2	
1	2	6	2	4	2	
2	4	2	5	7	3	9
3	3	0	2	5	8	4	6
4	7	3	6	2		

Key:
1|2 stands for 12

Draw this as an ordered stem and leaf diagram.

2 Keith has a job that involves driving to different shops each day.
Here are the distances, in kilometres, that he drove during April.

| 8 | 10 | 21 | 17 | 9 | 31 | 22 | 6 | 9 | 15 |
| 17 | 22 | 17 | 14 | 39 | 25 | 26 | 18 | 12 | 27 |

Draw a stem and leaf diagram to represent these data.

3 Here is a stem and leaf diagram showing the numbers of cars sold by a garage group over each of a number of weeks.

```
0 | 9
1 | 2 6 7 8
2 | 1 3 5 5 5 6 6 6 6
3 | 2 2 2 4 6 7
4 | 0
```

Key:
2|1 stands for 21 cars

a Write down the number of weeks represented in this diagram.
b Write down the mode for these data.
c Find the median number of cars.
d Work out the range of these data.

4 Here is a list of the number of minutes patients had to wait to see a dentist during one day at a dental surgery.

| 10 | 5 | 23 | 8 | 14 | 16 | 3 | 2 | 12 | 24 | 22 | 7 |
| 15 | 18 | 23 | 30 | 23 | 16 | 16 | 20 | 3 | 5 | 2 | 18 |

a Draw a stem and leaf diagram for these data.
b Write down the mode for these data.
c Find the median of these data.
d Work out the range of these data.

3.7 Using frequency tables to find averages for discrete data

Objective

You can use a frequency table to find averages.

Why do this?

If your dance club was debating whether to move location it could work out the change to average journey time as this might affect membership levels.

Get Ready

When a die was thrown 30 times the number 6 came up 5 times.
a What was the frequency of the number 6?
b What was the sum of all the 6s added together?

Key Points

- The mode is the number that has the highest frequency.
- The median is the number that is the middle value or halfway between the middle values if there are two of them.
- The mean is the sum of the values divided by the number of values (the number of values is the total frequency).
- For discrete data in a frequency table:

mean $= \dfrac{\sum f \times x}{\sum f}$ where f is the frequency, x is the variable and $\sum$ means 'the sum of'.

Example 21 The table shows information about the number of children in a sample of families.

Number of children in family	1	2	3	4	5
Frequency	3	11	9	5	6

   a Write down the mode of these data.

   b Find the median of these data.

   c Work out the mean of these data.

a The mode is 2 children. ← 2 has the highest frequency, which is 11.

b

Number of children in family x	Frequency f	Frequency × number of children $f \times x$
1	3	3
2	11	22
3	9	27
4	5	20
5	6	30
Total	34	102

There are 11 families with 2 children in each so the number of children is 11 × 2 = 22 children.

The total number of families is 34.

The total number of children is the sum of all the $f \times x$ values.

The total frequency is 34 so the median will be between the 17th and 18th values. ← There will be 16 values either side.

There are 3 families with 1 child in them.

There are 3 + 11 = 14 families with 2 or 1 children.

3 lies between the 14th and 23rd values.

There are 3 + 11 + 9 = 23 families with 3, 2 or 1 children.

The 17th and 18th values must both be 3.

The median is 3.

c The mean is $\dfrac{102}{34} = 3$ children. ← Mean $= \dfrac{\text{Total number of children}}{\text{Total number of families}} = \dfrac{\sum f \times x}{\sum f}$

Exercise 3I

1 A council wanted to provide extra parking on an estate.
   They asked a sample of households how many cars they had.
   The results are shown in the frequency table.

Number of cars	Frequency
0	0
1	10
2	7
3	6
4	2

   a Write down the mode of these data.
   b Find the median number of cars.
   c Work out the mean number of cars.

2 A sample of a tomato crop was taken and each tomato was weighed.
   The weights to the nearest 5 g are shown in the frequency table.

Weight of tomatoes	Frequency
55	2
60	5
65	10
70	6
75	2

   a Write down the mode of these data.
   b Find the median weight of the tomatoes.
   c Work out the mean weight of the tomatoes.

3 In an experiment with peas the number of peas per pod was recorded.
   The results are shown in the frequency table.

Number of peas per pod	Frequency
1	0
2	0
3	3
4	7
5	11
6	12
7	15
8	12
9	10

   a Write down the mode of these data.
   b Find the median number of peas per pod.
   c Work out the mean number of peas per pod.

3.8 Working with grouped data

◎ Objectives

- ○ You can find the modal class for grouped data.
- ○ You can find a class interval containing the median of grouped data.

◈ Why do this?

If you are collecting continuous data, such as times taken to swim 100 m, you need to have class intervals in your frequency table.

◈ Get Ready

1. Write whether each of the following types of data is continuous or discrete.
   a Number of items in a shopping basket
   b Size of feet
   c Waist size

2. Write down whether each statement is true or false.
   a $10 > 12$ b $0.1 < 0.2$ c $0.17 > 0.6$

◉ Key Points

- ◉ If you do not know the exact data in each class interval, you cannot give an exact value for the mode or the median and can only estimate the mean value.

- ◉ The class interval with the highest frequency is called the **modal class**.

- ◉ You can only write down the class interval in which the median falls.

Example 22   The frequency table gives information about the number of letters, l, in a sample of people's surnames.

Class interval	Frequency
3 to 5	1
6 to 8	3
9 to 11	5
12 to 13	4
14 to 15	2

> This is discrete data. No whole number appears in two classes.

> There will be $3 + 1 = 4$ values less than or equal to 8.

a Find the modal class.
b Find the class into which the median falls.

a The modal class is 9 to 11.

> Look for the class with the highest frequency.

b There are 15 names in total so the median will be the 8th value.
   There are $3 + 1 = 4$ names that are less than 8 letters long
   and $5 + 3 + 1 = 9$ names that are less than 12 letters long,
   so the median is in the class interval 9–11.

Example 23 The frequency table gives information about the lengths, l in mm, of leaves from a certain plant.

Class interval	Frequency f
$20 \leqslant l < 25$	6
$25 \leqslant l < 30$	8
$30 \leqslant l < 35$	13
$35 \leqslant l < 40$	14
$40 \leqslant l < 45$	9

This is continuous data.

There will be $6 + 8 = 14$ values less than 30.

a Find the modal class.

b Find the class into which the median falls.

a The modal class is $35 \leqslant l < 40$.

b There are 50 leaves so the median will be halfway between the 25th and 26th values.
There are 14 values less than 30 and 27 less than 35.
The median falls in the class $30 \leqslant l < 35$.

Exercise 3J

E

1 A group of students were asked how many times they visited a library in a term.
The results are shown in the frequency table.

Class interval	0 to 2	3 to 5	6 to 8	9 to 11
Frequency	0	6	10	6

a Write down the modal class.

b Find the class into which the median falls.

2 A group of students did a mental arithmetic test.
The results are shown in the frequency table.

Class interval	1 to 5	6 to 10	11 to 15	16 to 20
Frequency	1	9	15	5

a Write down the modal class.

b Find the class into which the median falls.

3 The frequency table gives the diameter, d in mm, of 48 balls of lead used in a quality control investigation.

a Write down the modal class.

b Find the class into which the median falls.

Class interval	Frequency
$0.7 \leqslant d < 0.9$	2
$0.9 \leqslant d < 1.1$	4
$1.1 \leqslant d < 1.3$	16
$1.3 \leqslant d < 1.5$	12
$1.5 \leqslant d < 1.7$	14

3.9 Estimating the mean of grouped data

Objective

- You can estimate the mean of grouped data.

Why do this?

If data is collected and arranged in a grouped frequency table, you will not have exact data values, so you won't be able to calculate the mean exactly. Using the middle values of the class intervals provides good estimates to work with.

Get Ready

Which number is halfway between:

a 6 and 8 **b** 56 and 64 **c** 75 and 76 **d** 0.75 and 0.85 **e** 100 000 and 150 000

Key Point

- An estimate for the mean of grouped data can be found by using the midpoint of the class interval and the formula $\dfrac{\sum fx}{\sum f}$ where f is the frequency and x is the class midpoint.

Example 24

Work out an estimate for the mean length of the people's surnames given in Example 22.

Class interval	Frequency f	Class midpoint x	$f \times x$
3 to 5	1	4	4
6 to 8	3	7	21
9 to 11	5	10	50
12 to 14	4	13	52
15 to 17	2	16	32
Totals	15		159

> The middle value of the class 3–5 is 4.

> The middle value of the class 6–8 is 7. The three people in the class 6–8 might not all have surnames 7 letters long. This is why it is an estimated mean.

$$\text{Estimated mean} = \frac{\sum f \times x}{\sum f} = \frac{159}{15} = 10.6$$

> You can now use the formula.

Example 25

Work out an estimate for the mean length of the leaves given in Example 23.

Class interval	Frequency f	Class midpoint x	$f \times x$
$20 \leqslant l < 25$	6	22.5	135
$25 \leqslant l < 30$	8	27.5	220
$30 \leqslant l < 35$	13	32.5	422.5
$35 \leqslant l < 40$	14	37.5	525
$40 \leqslant l < 45$	9	42.5	382.5
Totals	50		1685

ResultsPlus
Examiner's Tip

Remember to use the class midpoint when estimating the average.

$$\text{Estimated mean} = \frac{1685}{50} = 33.7 \text{ mm.}$$

Exercise 3K

1 In a healthy eating investigation the canteen supervisor at Conville College recorded the numbers of packets of crisps bought per month by a sample of students.
The results are shown in the frequency table.

Find an estimate for the mean number of crisps.

Class interval	Frequency f
1 to 3	1
4 to 6	9
7 to 9	15
10 to 12	5

A02 · C

2 A store is worried about the reliability of its lift. It records the number of times it breaks down each week over a period of 28 weeks.
The results are shown in the frequency table.
Find an estimate for the mean number of breakdowns.

Class interval	Frequency f
0 to 1	20
2 to 3	3
4 to 5	4
6 to 7	1

A02

3 Emma recorded the length of time (t), in minutes, each of her business phone calls took over a period of one month.
The results are shown in the frequency table.

Find an estimate for the mean time for her business phone calls.

Class interval	Frequency
$0 \leqslant t < 5$	9
$5 \leqslant t < 10$	10
$10 \leqslant t < 15$	9
$15 \leqslant t < 20$	7
$20 \leqslant t < 25$	5

A02

3.10 Using calculators

Objectives

● You use the calculator effectively and efficiently.
● You know how to enter complex calculations and use the function keys.
● You make sensible estimates of a range of measures.

Why do this?

You are less likely to make numerical mistakes when using a calculator, and many functions are difficult to do longhand.
By estimating the answer you can check any calculations for accuracy

Get Ready

Using BIDMAS, work out
a $3^2 \times (2 + 7)$ **b** $\dfrac{4^2 \times 3}{(5 + 3)}$

Using a calculator

Key Points

● The negative sign for **directed numbers** looks very much like the subtraction sign.
● Basic calculators have a change sign key $\boxed{+/-}$. To enter a number such as –6, press $\boxed{6}$ then press $\boxed{+/-}$.
● Scientific calculators have the negative sign $\boxed{(-)}$. To enter a number such as –6, press $\boxed{(-)}$ then $\boxed{6}$.
● The calculator display is limited to a certain number of figures. Where possible, avoid rounding until supplying a final answer. You can use the calculator's memory to help with more complicated numbers.

Example 26 Work out $\dfrac{(-6.5) + 2}{2}$.

On a basic calculator:

[6] [•] [5] [+/−] [+] [2] [÷] [2] [=] ← The display shows −2.25

On a scientific calculator:

[(] [(−)] [6] [•] [5] [+] [2] [)] [÷] [2] [=] ← The display shows −2.25

Finding roots and powers on a calculator

Key Points

- To work out **squares** use the x^2 button.

- To work out **cubes** some calculators have an x^3 button.

- To find a square root use the $\sqrt{\ }$ button.

- Scientific calculators have a power or index key x^y.

- There is also a root key $x^{\frac{1}{y}}$.

Example 27 Find **a** 4.2^2 **b** $\sqrt{4.84}$ **c** 3^4 **d** $\sqrt[4]{81}$.

a [4] [•] [2] [x^2] [=] ← The display shows 17.64.

b [$\sqrt{\ }$] [4] [•] [8] [4] [=] ← The display shows 2.2.

c [3] [x^y] [4] [=] ← The display shows 81.

d [8] [1] [$x^{\frac{1}{y}}$] [4] [=] ← The display shows 3.

Estimating

Key Points

- When doing a long calculation with decimals you can check your answer by calculating an estimate for the value.

Example 28 Estimate the value of $\dfrac{\sqrt{4.2} + 3.4}{2.3}$.

This is approximately $\dfrac{\sqrt{4} + 3}{2} = \dfrac{2 + 3}{2} = \dfrac{5}{2} = 2.5$ ← The actual value is 2.3693.

Exercise 3L

1 Find the values of:

    a 3.6^2 **b** 4.5^3 **c** $\sqrt{1806.25}$ **d** $\sqrt[3]{32768}$

2 The heights (m) of six male athletes are recorded as follows:

    1.62   1.67   1.84   1.77   1.68   1.82

    Find the mean height.

3 A librarian counts up the numbers of books on each shelf containing novels beginning with D. The data is as follows:

    41   29   28   31   42   50   52   29

    a Find the total number of books beginning with D.

    b Check your calculation by estimating the total number of books beginning with D.

4 **a** Estimate the value of $\dfrac{4.1^2 \times 2}{4.9}$.

    b Find the correct value of $\dfrac{4.1^2 \times 2}{4.9}$.

Chapter review

- The **mode** of a set of data is the value that occurs most frequently.

- The **median** is the middle value when the data are ordered from the smallest to the largest.

- If there are two middle values in a set of data the median is halfway between them.

- The **mean** of a set of data is the sum of the values divided by the total number of observations.

    $\text{Mean} = \dfrac{\text{sum of the values}}{\text{number of values}}$

- **Range** $=$ highest value $-$ lowest value

- To compare sets of data you need to give a measure of **average** and a measure of **spread**.

- A **stem and leaf diagram** makes it easy to find the mode, median and range of a set of data.

- For discrete data in a frequency table:

    $\text{mean} = \dfrac{\sum f \times x}{\sum f}$ where f is the frequency, x is the variable and $\sum$ means 'the sum of'.

- For **grouped data**:
  - the class interval with the highest frequency is called the **modal class**
  - you can only write down the class interval in which the median falls
  - an estimate for the mean of grouped data can be found by using the midpoint of the class interval.

Review exercise

F

1 Mary threw a dice 24 times.
Here are the 24 scores.

3 5 3 4 1 2 4 5 6 2 3 4
3 1 4 3 2 3 5 5 3 4 2 1

a Complete the frequency table.

b Write down the mode

Score	Tally	Frequency
1		
2		
3		
4		
5		
6		

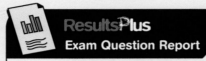

Exam Question Report

Most candidates did very well on part **a** of this question as they knew to write tallies and then show the frequencies

March 2007

E

2 The weekly incomes of five people are shown in the table.

a Work out the mean income per week.

b Work out the median income per week.

c Work out the range of weekly incomes.

d How much more did Mrs Chown earn than Mrs Basingi?

Name	Income
Mr Rahman	£420
Mrs Basingi	£365
Mr Clarke	£400
Mr Abson	£280
Mrs Chown	£430

3 Here are ten numbers.

7 6 8 4 5 9 7 3 6 7

a Work out the range.

b Work out the mean.

Nov 2008

4 Jason collected some information about the heights of 19 plants.
This information is shown in the stem and leaf diagram.

```
1 | 1  2  3  4
2 | 3  3  5  9  9
3 | 0  2  2  6  6  7
4 | 1  1  4  8
```

Key:
4|8 means 48 mm

Find the median.

Nov 2008

5 Peter rolled a 6-sided dice ten times.
Here are his scores.

3 2 4 6 3 3 4 2 5 4

a Work out the median of his scores.

b Work out the mean of his scores.

c Work out the range of his scores.

June 2007

6 Here are the weights, in kg, of 8 people.

63 65 65 70 72 86 90 97

a Write down the mode of the 8 weights.

b Work out the range of the weights.

June 2007

7 Rachel is going to make a batch of shortbread biscuits.
She mixes:

110 g of butter   50 g sugar   175 g plain flour

Each biscuit uses 22 g of mixture.

a Work out the largest number of biscuits Rachel can make.

Tom decides to make a batch of oat crunchies.
He mixes:

50 g jumbo oats   60 g porridge oats   80 g brown sugar   110 g margarine

He makes 12 oat crunchies all the same size and has no mixture left.

b How much mixture did he use for each oat crunchie?

8 Five positive numbers have a mode of 5, a median of 5 and a mean of 4.
Write down as many possible combinations of five numbers that give these statistics as you can.

9 The stem and leaf diagram shows the ages, in years, of all the workers in a small factory.

```
2 | 0  2  2  5  7
3 | 3  4  4  4  4  5                Key:
4 | 5  6  6  6  6  8  9  9  9       4|5 stands for 45 years
5 | 2  4  4  6  7  9
6 | 0  2  5
```

a Work out the number of workers.

b Write down the mode of these data.

c Find the median of these data.

d Work out the range of these data.

10 A group of girls went to a college dance. They each bought a new dress.
The costs of the dresses were

£22   £22   £22   £28   £32   £36   £40   £40   £45   £180

a Write down the mode of these data.

b Find the median price

c Work out the mean price.

d Which of the three averages worked out in parts a, b and c best describes the price the girls paid?
Give a reason for your answer.

11 Samples of apples were taken from two trees. One was an eating apple tree and the other was a cooking apple tree.
The weights of the apples were

Eating apple	135	135	140	138	142	150	132
Cooking apple	140	136	150	160	138	162	150

a Find the means and ranges for these data.

b Compare the frequency distributions of the weights of
the two types of apple.

D

12 Zoe recorded the weights, in kilograms, of 15 people.
Here are her results.

87 51 46 77 74 58 68 78
48 63 52 64 79 60 66

a Complete the ordered stem and leaf diagram to show these results.

b Write down the number of people with a weight of more than 70 kg.

c Work out the range of the weights.

4	
5	
6	
7	
8	

March 2009

13 Zach has 10 CDs.
The table gives some information about the number of tracks on each CD.

a Write down the mode.

b Work out the mean.

Number of cups	Frequency	
11	1	
12	3	
13	0	
14	2	
15	4	

June 2009

ResultsPlus
Exam Question Report

81% of students answered part **b** of this question poorly.

14 Here are the ages, in years, of 15 teachers.

35 52 42 27 36
23 31 41 50 34
44 28 45 45 53

Draw an ordered stem and leaf diagram to show this information. You must include a key.   *May 2008 adapted*

15 Explain why the sentence 'The majority of spiders in this country have more than the average number of legs' can be true. You need to state which average is being used.

16 Ali found out the number of rooms in each of 40 houses in a town.
He used the information to complete the frequency table.

Number of rooms	Frequency	
4	4	
5	7	
6	10	
7	12	
8	5	
9	2	

Ali said that the mode is 9. Ali is wrong.

a Explain why.

b Calculate the mean number of rooms.   *Nov 2007*

17 A group of university students did a maths test. The table shows their scores.

Males	42	22	65	42	70	50	45
Females	25	90	55	26	95	50	87

Using your understanding of averages and ranges, compare the males' and the females' scores.

18 One teacher is responsible for the distribution of milk at break time in each school.

There are p classes and each class is sent $x + 2$ bottles of milk, where x is the number of children present in a class.

The teacher uses $\Sigma x + 2p$ to work out how many bottles are needed.

a Is $\Sigma x + 2p$ an expression, an equation or a formula?

There are 80 children in Banjo school.
The numbers attending Banjo school one day are shown in the table.

Class	1	2	3	4
Numbers attending	20	18	18	20

b Work out the number of bottles of milk required for that day.

c The dairy send Banjo school 84 bottles of milk per day.
  Discuss whether or not you think this is a suitable number.

*** 19** Class 5A take six maths tests every year, each one out of 100. Meena has a mean score of 64 marks per test for the first five tests of the year. Her parents have promised her a bicycle if she can achieve a mean score of 70. What mark would she have to get in the sixth test to achieve this mean score?

20 A small factory pays salaries to 8 workers, a manager and an owner.
The salaries they earn are shown in the table.

	Salary
Workers	£10 000
Manager	£40 000
Owner	£180 000

Depending on the average you use, the average wage of people in the factory is vastly different.
If you were negotiating for a higher salary, which average would you use?
If you were negotiating to keep the salaries low, which average would you use?
Explain your answers.

21 The hourly wages, in pounds, of the employees in a factory were recorded.
The results are shown in the frequency table.

Hourly wage £s	7 to 9	10 to 12	13 to 15	16 to 18	19 to 21
Frequency	5	20	20	10	5

a Write down the modal class of these data.

b Find the class interval that contains the median hourly wage.

c Estimate the mean hourly wage.

C **A02**

22 Oliver measured the heights (h), in cm, of the leek plants in his garden.
Here are his results.

Class interval	Frequency
$25 \leqslant h < 27$	5
$27 \leqslant h < 29$	10
$29 \leqslant h < 31$	13
$31 \leqslant h < 33$	15
$33 \leqslant h < 35$	7

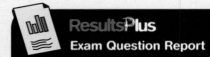

Results Plus
Exam Question Report

91% of students scored poorly on this question because they did not use the midpoint of the range to find the mean of grouped data.

a Write down the modal class.

b Find the class into which the median height falls.

c Work out an estimate for the mean height of the leeks.

23 Josh asked 30 students how many minutes they each took to get to school.
The table shows some information about his results.
Work out an estimate for the mean number of minutes taken by the 30 students.

Time (t minutes)	Frequency
$0 < t \leqslant 10$	6
$10 < t \leqslant 20$	11
$20 < t \leqslant 30$	8
$30 < t \leqslant 40$	5

Nov 2008

24 Vanessa made 80 phone calls last month.
The table gives information about the length of the calls.

Length of call (t minutes)	Frequency	
$0 < t \leqslant 10$	20	
$10 < t \leqslant 20$	32	
$20 < t \leqslant 30$	14	
$30 < t \leqslant 40$	9	
$40 < t \leqslant 50$	5	

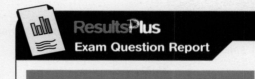

Results Plus
Exam Question Report

86% of students answered this question poorly.

Work out an estimate for the mean length of the calls.

March 2008

25 80 people work in Joe's factory.
The table shows some information about the annual pay of these 80 workers.

Annual pay (£x)	Number of workers
$10\,000 < x \leqslant 14\,000$	32
$14\,000 < x \leqslant 16\,000$	24
$16\,000 < x \leqslant 18\,000$	16
$18\,000 < x \leqslant 20\,000$	6
$20\,000 < x \leqslant 40\,000$	2

a Write down the modal class interval.

b Find the class interval that contains the median.

June 2007

4 LINE DIAGRAMS AND SCATTER GRAPHS

Life expectancy over time is one variable often represented using a line graph. The line for life expectancy in the UK shows a continual increase from 1980 to the present day. In 1980, a man could expect to live to an age of about 71 years whilst the average life expectancy for a woman was 77. By 2009, the life expectancy for both sexes had gone up considerably, with average life expectancy for a baby girl at 81.5 years and for a baby boy at 77.2 years.

Objectives

In this chapter you will:
- learn to produce and interpret line graphs and scatter graphs
- see if there is any linear association between two variables
- be able to draw lines of best fit
- be able to distinguish between positive, negative and zero correlation
- use a line of best fit to predict values of a variable.

Before you start

You need to:
- know that letters can represent numbers
- be able to collect like terms
- know simple number bonds.

4.1 Plotting points on a graph

Objectives

● You can plot and interpret graphs that model real situations.

Why do this?

There are a number of situations in which varying one thing causes another to vary. For example, the more electricity you consume, the more expensive your bill.

Plotting points on a graph

Key Points

● The coordinates of a point P are written (x, y) where x is the distance across the graph and y is the distance up the graph.

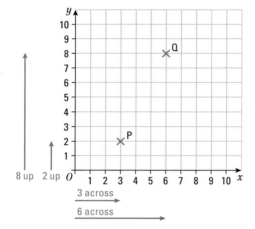

Point P is (3, 2). The x coordinate comes first and the y coordinate comes second.

Point Q is (6, 8).

Plotting the graph of a formula

Key Points

● To plot the graph of a formula, find pairs of corresponding values and use them as coordinates for the graph.

Example 1

a Plot the graph of $y = x$ for values of x between 0 and 5. ⟵ *Remember: x means $1x$.*

b Find the value of y when $x = 2.5$ using your graph.

c Find the value of x which gives a value of 4.5 to y.

a

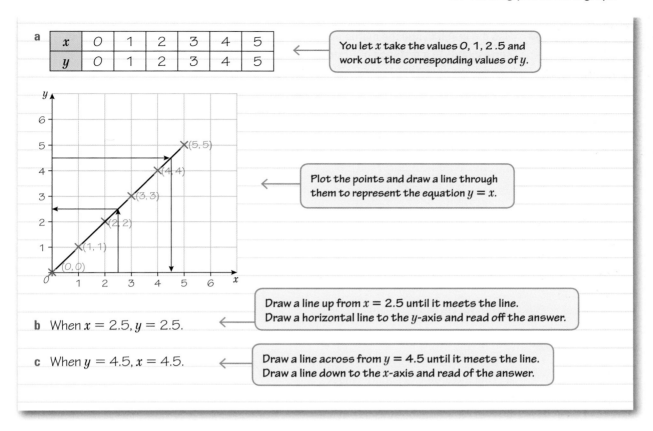

x	0	1	2	3	4	5
y	0	1	2	3	4	5

> You let x take the values 0, 1, 2 .5 and work out the corresponding values of y.

> Plot the points and draw a line through them to represent the equation $y = x$.

> Draw a line up from $x = 2.5$ until it meets the line. Draw a horizontal line to the y-axis and read off the answer.

b When $x = 2.5$, $y = 2.5$.

> Draw a line across from $y = 4.5$ until it meets the line. Draw a line down to the x-axis and read of the answer.

c When $y = 4.5$, $x = 4.5$.

Real-life graphs

Example 2 This graph shows the number of pounds you get for a number of US dollars ($) at an exchange rate of $1 = £0.60.

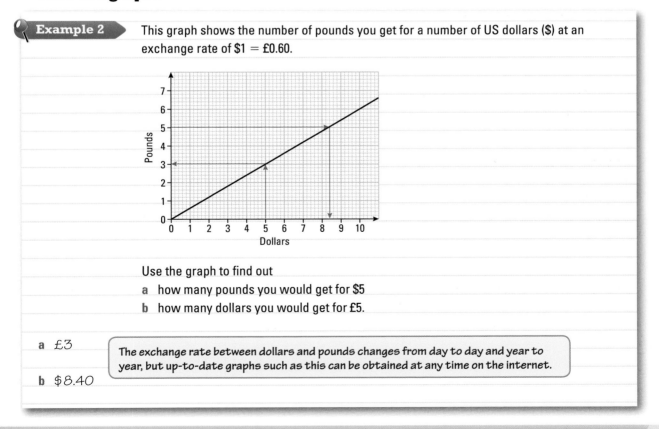

Use the graph to find out

a how many pounds you would get for $5

b how many dollars you would get for £5.

a £3

> The exchange rate between dollars and pounds changes from day to day and year to year, but up-to-date graphs such as this can be obtained at any time on the internet.

b $8.40

Example 3 Use the graph to find the metric equivalent of 5.2 miles and the distance in miles that corresponds to a distance of 10 km.

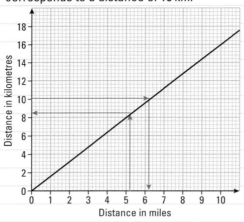

Distance in kilometres

Distance in miles

This is a conversion graph.

5.2 miles = 8.4 km and 10 km = 6.2 miles.

Example 4 This graph shows the relationship between length of side and area.

    a Find the area of a square whose sides are 3.6 cm long.

    b Find the length of sides of a square that has an area of 2 cm².

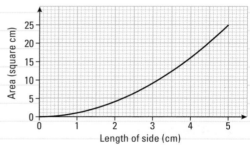

Area (square cm)

Length of side (cm)

a $13\,cm^2$

b $1.4\,cm$

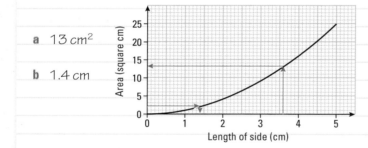

Area (square cm)

Length of side (cm)

Exercise 4A

Questions in this chapter are targeted at the grades indicated.

E

1 This graph shows the number of pounds you get for a number of euros.

    a Estimate the number of pounds you can get for 7.75 euros.

    b Estimate the number of euros you can get for £5.00.

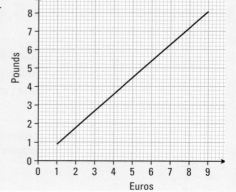

Pounds

Euros

2 This graph shows the relationship between the diameter of an orange and its surface area.

    a Estimate the surface area if the diameter is 5.5 cm.

    b Estimate the diameter if the surface area is 50 cm^2.

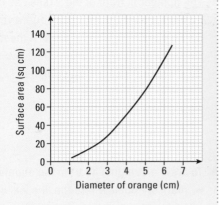

E

3   **a** Copy and complete the following table.

    b Plot the graph of the line $y = 2x$ for values of x between 0 and 5.
Use values 0 to 6 on the x-axis and 0 to 12 on the y-axis.

    c Use your graph to find the value of y when x is 2.5.

    d Use your graph to find the value of x when y is 7.

x	0	1	2	3	4	5
$y = 2x$	0	2	4			

D

4.2 Straight-line graphs

◎ Objectives

● You can recognise and plot equations that correspond to straight-line graphs, including gradients.

⊘ Why do this?

If you do an experiment to see how far a spring stretches when different weights are put on it, you should be able to predict from your experiment how much it stretches for a given weight, and what weight would make it stretch a certain amount.

⬆ Get Ready

1. In the formula $y = x + 3$, find y for the following values of x.
    a $x = 0$ **b** $x = 2$ **c** $x = 5$
2. Plot the graph of $y = x + 3$ for values of x between 0 and 5.

◉ Key Points

◉ The equation of a straight-line graph can be written in the form $y = mx + c$. The number on its own (c) tells you where the straight line crosses the y-axis.
Here are five straight-line graphs.
    $y = x + 3$
    $y = x + 2$
    $y = x + 1$
    $y = x + 0$
    $y = x - 1$

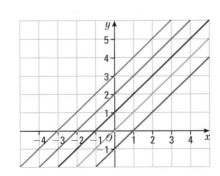

◉ The number in front of the x tells you the steepness of the line. If the
number is positive, for each square you move to the right you move up
by the number in front of the x. If the number is negative, for each square
you move to the right you move down by the number in front of the x.
Here are four straight-line graphs.

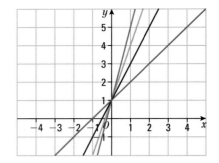

$$y = x + 1$$
$$y = 2x + 1$$
$$y = 3x + 1$$
$$y = 4x + 1$$

◉ To draw a straight line from the equation:

  ◉ mark the point where the line will cross the y-axis

  ◉ find out how many squares you go up (or down) each square you move to the right (or left) from the number
in front of the x

  ◉ join up the points with a straight line.

Example 5   Draw a graph of the equation $y = 1.5x + 2$ for the values from $x = 0$ to $x = 4$

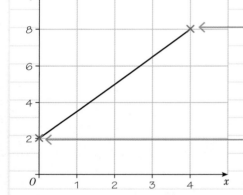

When $x = 4, y = 1.5 \times 4 + 2 = 8$

These two points fix the position of the line.

The line is drawn between them.

When $x = 0, y = 2$

Example 6   The graph shows a straight-line graph, representing the equation $y = mx + c$, where m
and c are fixed numbers. Find the equation of this line.

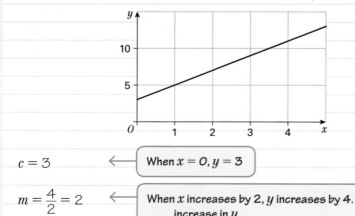

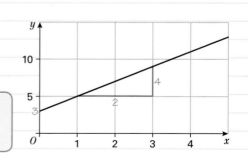

$c = 3$ ⟵   When $x = 0, y = 3$

$m = \dfrac{4}{2} = 2$ ⟵   When x increases by 2, y increases by 4.
$$m = \frac{\text{increase in } y}{\text{increase in } x}$$

$y = 2x + 3$

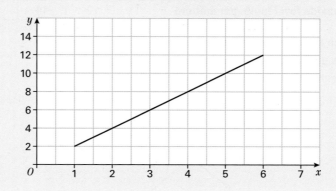

Exercise 4B

1 **a** Draw axes for 0 to 8 on the x-axis and 0 to 18 on the y-axis.

x	2	3	4	5	6	7
y	2	5	8	11	14	17

    b Plot the points shown in the table on these axes.

    c Join the points with a straight line.

    d Work out the gradient of the line.

D

2 The gradient of a line is $\frac{3}{2}$.
For this line write down the increase in y for every one increase in x.

3 Find the gradient of the line.

C

4.3 Drawing and using line graphs

Objectives

- You can draw line graphs.
- You can estimate values from a line graph.

Why do this?

If you collect data using an experiment you can often see how one thing changes as you change another thing. For example, you might record the amounts of carbon monoxide in a busy street at different times of day.

You can use a line graph to represent these data.

Get Ready

The graph shows two plotted points.
a Write down the coordinates of the two points.
b A third point has coordinates (2, 2.5); add this point to a copy of the graph and draw a straight line through the points.

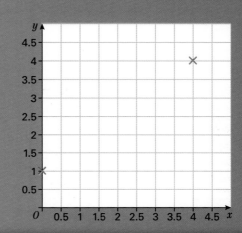

🔍 **Key Points**

◉ If you have a sample size of 10 and you make a single observation of each member you will have 10 observations, for example people's heights. You could, however, make two observations of each member, for example height and weight, and you will then have 10 pairs of observations.

◉ Pairs of observations can be plotted on a line graph.

Example 7 The table below gives information about the levels of carbon monoxide in a busy street.

Time of day	04:00	08:00	12:00	16:00	00:00	04:00
Carbon monoxide level (parts per million)	1	2	14	18	9	1

a Draw a line graph for these data.
b When was the amount of carbon monoxide at its highest?
c When was the amount of carbon monoxide at its lowest?

a

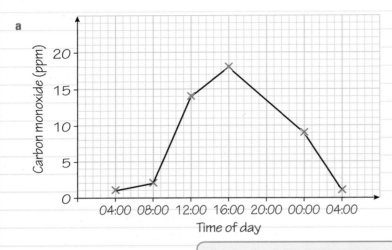

> Plot the points on the graph.
> Join the points with straight lines.

b 16:00 hours ← Find when the highest value occurs.

c 04:00 hours ← Find when the lowest value occurs.

Example 8 The line graph shows the rate at which water flows in a river measured on the same day for each month of a year.

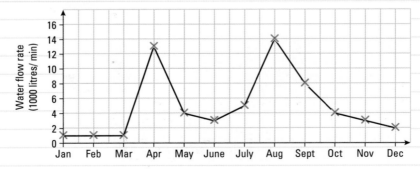

a Which month had the highest water flow rate?
b When was it lowest?

a August. ← | This will be the highest point. |

b January, February and March.

↑ | It remains the same for these three months. |

| In both of the above examples time was the variable along the x-axis. This is often the case with line graphs. It is clear that there is no pattern to these two graphs. |

Exercise 4C

E

1 Abbie has a pay-as-you-go mobile phone.
She pays 40p for each minute she uses her phone.
The graph shows the cost of using the phone.

a How much does it cost Abbie to use her phone for 32 minutes?

b One month Abbie spent £8.40 on using her phone.
For how many minutes did Abbie use her phone that month?

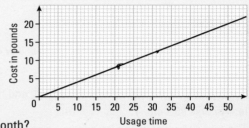

2 This graph converts temperatures between Fahrenheit and Celsius.

a Use the graph to convert these temperatures to degrees Fahrenheit.
    i 20°C   **ii** 100°C   **iii** 36°C

b Use the graph to convert these temperatures to degrees Celsius.
    i 140°F   **ii** 60°F   **iii** 88°F

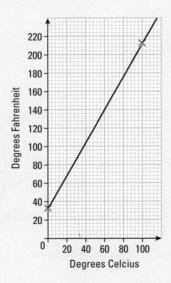

* 3 A man sells cornets from an ice cream van.
He kept a tally of the number of cornets sold during the seven hours he worked one day.
During the day he sold a total of 500 cornets.
The table shows how many cornets he had sold, in total, by the end of each hour.

Hours	0	1	2	3	4	5	6	7
Cornets sold	0	10	30	150	260	300	320	500

a Draw a line graph for these data.

b Write down the hour in which he sold the most cornets.

4.4 Drawing and using scatter graphs

Objectives

● You can use a scatter graph to see if there is any relationship between pairs of variables.

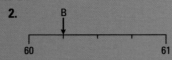

Why do this?

Do people who are tall have larger feet? To investigate such problems a scatter graph can be drawn.

Get Ready

What are the values of points A to D?

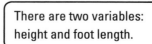

Key Point

● A **scatter graph** shows whether there is any relationship between two variables.

For example, Christopher was 168 cm tall and his foot length was 25.1 cm.
The grid shows how he plotted this point on a graph.

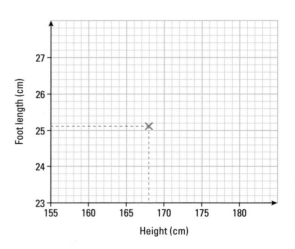

The table shows the heights and foot lengths of seven other boys.

Height (cm)	159	166	167	170	170	171	175
Foot length (cm)	24.0	24.8	24.5	25.4	25	25.7	26.0

Each of these pairs of values is plotted on the graph in the same way.
The resulting graph is called a scatter diagram or scatter graph.

The scatter graph shows the heights and foot lengths, in cm, of all eight boys.

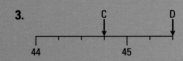

The pairs of values are plotted on the graph in the usual way. This cross shows Height 171, Foot length 25.7.

There are two variables: height and foot length.

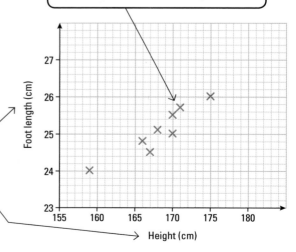

There seems to be a relationship between the boys' heights and foot lengths: the greater the height, the longer the foot length.

Example 9

The table below shows, for Ford Focus cars, the engine size, in litres, and the average distance (miles) they can travel on 1 gallon of petrol.

Engine size (*l*)	1.4	1.6	1.8	2.0	2.5
Miles per gallon	42.8	42.2	40.3	39.8	30.4

a   Draw a scatter graph for these data.

b   Comment on the relationship between engine size and the average miles per gallon.

a

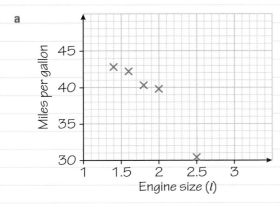

b   There seems to be a relationship:
the bigger the engine the fewer miles they can travel
on one gallon of petrol.

> Look to see if there is a pattern.
> State what the pattern is.

Exercise 4D

1   A health clinic recorded the pulse rates, in beats per minute, and the breathing rates, in breaths per minute, of 12 people. The scatter graph shows this information.

Describe the relationship between breaths per minute and pulse rate.

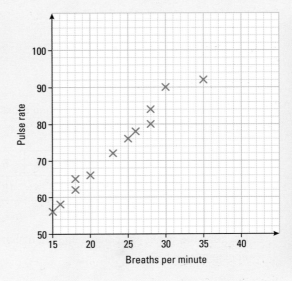

D

D

2 The heights and weights of 10 children in Year 7 are shown in the table.

Height (cm)	140	150	145	150	170	180	160	155	160	165
Weight (kg)	36	35	40	42	62	75	50	50	55	60

a Using the scales shown on the diagram, draw a scatter graph for these data.

b Describe the relationship between height and weight.

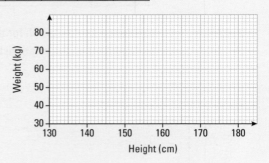

A02
A03

3 The data table shows the weight and top speeds of nine cars.

Weight (kg)	800	900	1000	1100	1200	1400	1500	1600	1700
Top speed (mph)	90	90	100	105	110	115	120	120	125

a Using the scales shown on the diagram, draw a scatter graph for these data.

b Describe the relationship between weight and top speed.

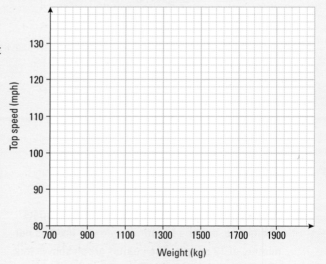

* **4** The data show the number of pedestrian crossings and the number of pedestrian accidents in each of 12 areas over a period of six months.

Number of crossings	10	8	15	6	12	11	9	16	18	12	5	9
Number of accidents	7	10	4	10	4	8	6	3	2	3	16	7

Draw a scatter graph for these data.

Describe the relationship between the number of pedestrian crossings and the number of pedestrian accidents.

4.5 Recognising correlation

◎ Objective

○ You can distinguish between positive, negative and zero correlation.

⌖ Why do this?

To get your driving license you have to take a theory test and a driving test. Is there a relationship between these two? If there is, the two are correlated. It is important to be able to determine what sort of correlation there is.

⬥ Get Ready

The number of visitors per month for a 5-month period to an outdoor water park are as follows:
7675   5536   2462   1021   500.
Can you suggest which months these are?

Key Points

◉ On the two scatter graphs in Section 4.4, it appears that there is a pattern: as one variable changes so does the other variable. We say they are correlated. A relationship between pairs of variables is called a **correlation**.

◉ If one variable increases as the other one increases the correlation is said to be positive. For example, in the case of height and foot length, the foot length increases as the height increases, so the correlation is positive.

◉ If one variable decreases as the other increases the correlation is said to be negative. For example, in the case of engine size and the number of miles per gallon, as the engine size increases the number of miles per gallon decreases, so the correlation is negative.

◉ If there is no relationship between the variables then there is no correlation and the correlation is said to be zero. These three possibilities are shown on the right.

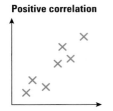

Positive correlation

As one value increases the other one increases.

Negative correlation

As one value increases the other decreases.

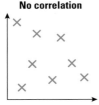

No correlation

The points are random and widely spaced.

Example 10

A factory owner thought that older men performed a task at a quicker rate than young men. The scatter graph shows the ages of 12 men and the time it took them to do the task.

a Describe the correlation.
b Describe the relationship between age and time taken to do the task.
c Was the factory owner right?

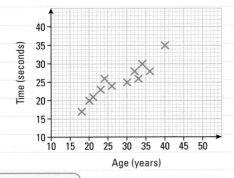

As one variable goes up so does the other one.

a Positive correlation. ←
b The greater the age the longer it took to do the task.
c The factory owner was wrong.

Exercise 4E

D

1 The scatter graph shows the marks achieved by a group of 10 students in a physics exam and in a woodwork exam.

Describe the correlation shown by this scatter graph.

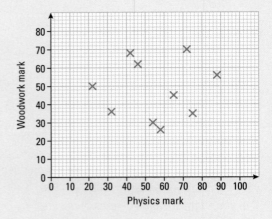

A03

2 A garage sells second-hand cars. The scatter graph shows the ages and costs of 10 luxury cars of the same model.

a Describe the correlation.

b Describe the relationship between age and cost.

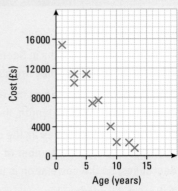

A03

3 Copy and complete the following table. Tick the type of correlation for each set of data.

Variables	Positive correlation	Negative correlation	No corrrelation
Height and Weight of people			
Intelligence and Weight of people			
Size of garden and Number of birds			
Age and Running speed of adults			
Height and Shoe size of people			
Age of cars and Engine size			
Arm length and Leg length of people			

*4 Jacob sells bottled water from a market stall. He likes hot days because he thinks that he will sell more bottles. For 10 days he records the number of bottles of water that he sells. He also gets the maximum temperature for each day from a website.

The data he collects are shown in the table.

Maximum temperature (°C)	19	27	18	24	30	22	23	16	25	27
Number of bottles of water sold	50	80	50	64	90	60	65	45	70	75

a Draw a scatter graph for these data.

b Describe the correlation and explain what this means.

4.6 Lines of best fit

⊙ You can draw lines of best fit by eye.

? Why do this?

A line of best fit acts as a model for the relationship. A line of best fit smoothes out the irregularities that are due to other things.

◆ Get Ready

Look again at the scatter graph in question 2 on p. 96 about the correlation between the age of a garage's cars and their cost. How much would you expect an 8-year-old car to cost?

Key Points

⊙ If the points on a scatter graph lie approximately in a straight line, the correlation is said to be **linear**. The word 'linear' means in a straight line.
⊙ If the points are roughly in a straight line you can draw a **line of best fit** through them.
⊙ A line of best fit is a straight line that passes as near as possible to the various points so as to best represent the trend of the graph. It does not have to pass through any of the points, but it might pass through some of them.
⊙ There should be roughly the same number of points either side of the line and the line drawn should best represent the trend of the points.

If lines of best fit were added to the scatter graphs of height and foot length in Section 4.4 and miles per gallon and engine size in Example 9, they would look like this.

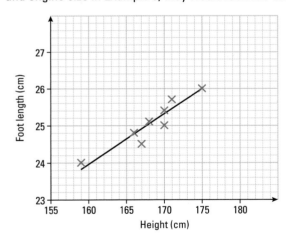
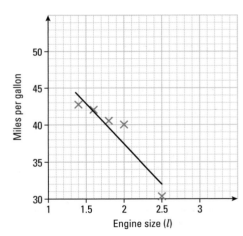

Example 11

The heights, in cm, and the weights, in kg, of 10 children are recorded.
The table below shows information about the results.

Height (cm)	38	40	42	43	45	49	49	50	51	53
Weight (kg)	145	148	147	151	152	155	157	158	160	164

a Draw a scatter graph of these data.
b Describe the correlation between the weight and height of these children.
c Draw a line of best fit on your scatter graph.

a

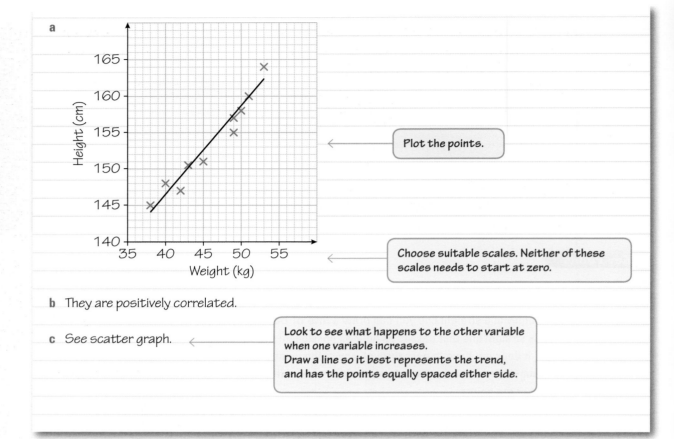

Plot the points.

Choose suitable scales. Neither of these scales needs to start at zero.

b They are positively correlated.

c See scatter graph.

Look to see what happens to the other variable when one variable increases.
Draw a line so it best represents the trend, and has the points equally spaced either side.

Exercise 4F

D

1 The scatter graph shows the engine sizes and the distance travelled on a litre of petrol for 10 different cars.

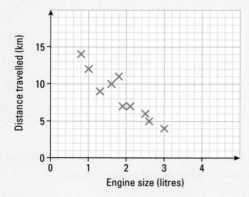

a Describe the correlation.

b Copy the scatter diagram.

c Draw a line of best fit on your diagram.

d Describe the relationship between engine size and distance travelled.

A03

2 A company has a hairdressing shop in each of 10 towns. The director of the company plans to expand into other towns. To make sensible decisions he has to look at profits and town sizes for the shops he already has. This information is shown in the table.

Town size (1000s)	11	15	16	20	26	30	35	42	45	50
Annual profits (£1000s)	42	46	45	48	55	50	54	58	65	70

a Copy the scatter graph and plot the remaining points.

b Describe the correlation.

c Draw a line of best fit on your diagram.

d Describe the relationship between town size and profits.

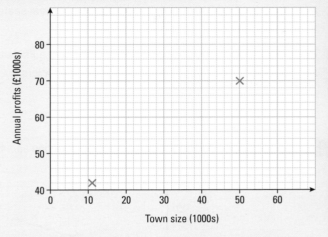

3 An NHS Trust has seven hospitals. Some data on the average number of operations and the number of operating theatres for each hospital are shown in the table.

Number of operating theatres	2	4	5	5	6	7	8
Average number of operations per week	60	80	90	85	100	130	150

a Copy the diagram and complete the scatter graph for these data.

b Describe the correlation.

c Draw a line of best fit on your diagram.

d Describe the relationship between the number of operating theatres and the average number of operations per week.

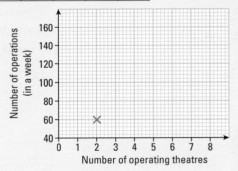

4.7 Using lines of best fit to make predictions

◎ Objective

○ You can use a line of best fit to predict a value of one of a pair of variables given a value for the other variable.

⊘ Why do this?

An ice cream man could use a line of best fit to estimate the number of sales when the temperature increases.

⬆ Get Ready

Look again at the Get Ready for Section 4.3. What do you think the next value might be?

Key Points

- If a value of one of the variables is known you can estimate the corresponding value of the other by using the line of best fit.

  For example, to estimate the height of a child weighing 47 kg, using the graph from Example 5, you draw a vertical line at 47 kg until it meets the line of best fit. You then draw a horizontal line from there and read off where it comes on the vertical scale. In this case, you read off 155 cm.

- Using the line of best fit to obtain answers that are outside the range of the plotted points may give unreliable answers.

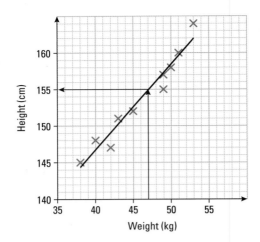

Example 12 The scatter graph gives information about the reaction times, in milliseconds, of adult women.

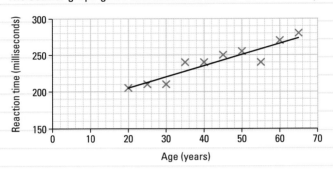

a Estimate the reaction time of a woman of 56.

b Estimate the age of a woman whose reaction time is 250 milliseconds.

c Explain why you would not estimate outside the range of readings with this scatter graph.

a 260 milliseconds.

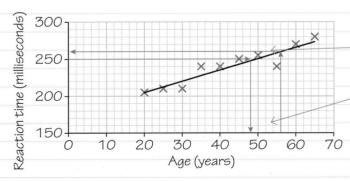

> For part **a**, draw a line from 56 up to the line of best fit. From where it meets the line draw a horizontal line across to the vertical axis and read off the required value.

> For part **b**, draw a horizontal line from 250 on the vertical axis across to the line of best fit. From where it meets the line draw a vertical line down to the horizontal axis and read off the required value.

b 48 years.

c If you extend the line to age 0 you find a newborn child has a reaction time of 170 milliseconds, which is obviously silly. If you extend in the other direction a person with a reaction time of 420 would be about 120 years old.

ResultsPlus
Examiner's Tip

Always draw in the lines – you may get method marks for this even if they are in the wrong place.

C

Exercise 4G

1   A factory makes model cars. The scatter diagram shows
some information about the numbers of models made and
the cost of making them.
  a   Describe the correlation.
  b   Use the graph and the line of best fit to find an estimate for:
   i   the cost of making 50 000 models
   ii   the number you can make for £45 000.

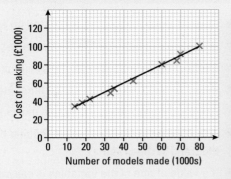

2   The scatter graph shows the midday temperature and the number of units of electricity used by a house
on each of 10 days.

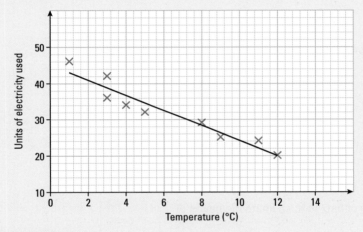

  a   Describe the correlation.
  b   Use the graph and the line of best fit to find an estimate for:
   i   the number of units of electricity used when the midday temperature was 7°C
   ii   the midday temperature when 35 units of electricity were used.

3   The following scatter graph shows the ages and blood pressures of a group of 10 men.

A02
A03

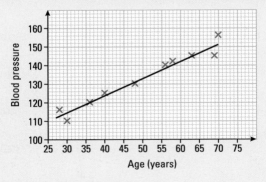

  a   Estimate the blood pressure of a man aged 65.
  b   Predict the age of a man whose blood pressure is 135.
  c   Describe the relationship between age and blood pressure.

Chapter review

⊚ Pairs of observations can be plotted on a line graph.

⊚ A relationship between pairs of variables is called a **correlation**.

⊚ If one variable increases as the other increases the correlation is said to be positive.

⊚ If one variable decreases as the other increases the correlation is said to be negative.

⊚ If there is no relationship between the variables then there is **no correlation** and the correlation is said to be zero.

⊚ A **line of best fit** is a straight line that passes as near as possible to the various points so as to best represent the trend of the graph.

⊚ If a value of one of the variables is known you can estimate the corresponding value of the other by using the line of best fit.

Review exercise

1 The scatter graph shows some information about 10 students.
It shows the arm length and the height of each student.

  a What type of correlation does this scatter graph show?

  b Draw a line of best fit on a copy of the scatter graph.

Another student has an arm length of 75 cm.

  c Use your line of best fit to estimate the height of this student.

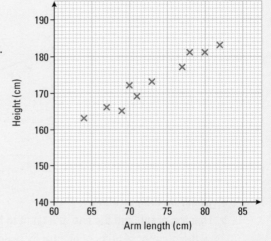

March 2009

2 A superstore sells the Clicapic digital camera.
The price of the camera changes each week.
Each week the manager records the price of the camera and the number of cameras sold that week.
The scatter graph shows this information.

  a Describe the relationship between the price of the camera and the number of cameras sold.

  b Draw a line of best fit on the scatter graph.

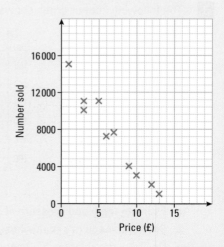

Nov 2008

3 Some students revised for a mathematics exam. They used an internet revision site.
The scatter graph shows the amount of time seven students spent on the internet revision site and the marks the students got in the mathematics exam.

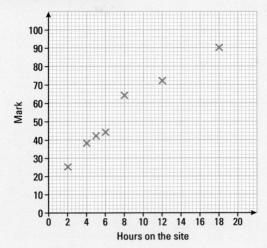

Here is the information for 3 more students.

Hours on the site	7	10	16
Mark	50	56	78

a Plot this information on a copy of the scatter graph.
b What type of correlation does this scatter graph show?
c Draw a line of best fit on your scatter graph.

Nov 2008

4 The scatter graph shows some information about the age, in years, of apprentices and the time, in minutes, it takes them to learn a certain skill.
A line of best fit is drawn on the graph.
a Work out an estimate for the gradient of the line of best fit.
b Use the line of best fit to estimate how long it would take a 16.5 year old to learn the skill.
c Describe the correlation.
d What conclusions can you draw about the time it takes apprentices to learn skills?

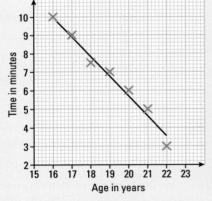

* 5 The table gives information about the marks gained by 10 students in a French exam and in a German exam. The exam was marked out of 50.

Student	A	B	C	D	E	F	G	H	I	J
French	10	10	18	25	28	33	39	42	43	46
German	11	14	21	26	35	32	42	42	45	50

a Draw a scatter diagram for these data.
b Draw in a line of best fit.
c Work out the gradient of the line of best fit.
d Work out the proportion of students that got less than 26 in at least one of the exams.

C

6 The scatter graph shows information for some weather stations.
It shows the height of each weather station above sea level (m) and the mean July midday temperature (°C) for that weather station.

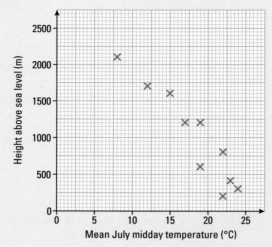

The table shows this information for two more weather stations.

Height of weather station above sea level	1000	500
Mean July midday temperature (°C)	20	22

a Plot this information on the scatter graph.

b What type of correlation does this scatter graph show?

c Draw a line of best fit on a copy of the scatter graph.

A weather station is 1800 metres above sea level.
d Estimate the mean July midday temperature for this weather station.

At another weather station the mean July midday temperature is 18°C.
e Estimate the height above sea level of this weather station.

June 2008

7 The scatter graph shows some information about the ages and values of fourteen cars.
The cars are the same make and type.

a Describe the relationship between the age of a car and its value in pounds.

b Draw a line of best fit on a copy of the scatter graph.

A car is 3 years old.
c Use your line of best fit to find an estimate of its value.

A car has a value of £3500.
d Use your line of best fit to find an estimate of its age.

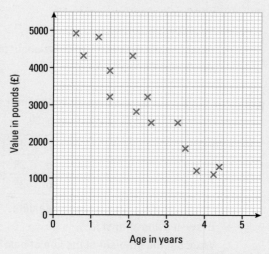

March 2008

8 Jake recorded the weight, in kg, and the height, in cm, of each of ten children.
The scatter graph shows information about his results.

  a Describe the relationship between the weight and the height of these children.

  b Draw a line of best fit on a copy the scatter graph.

  c Use your line of best fit to estimate the height of a child whose weight is 47 kg.

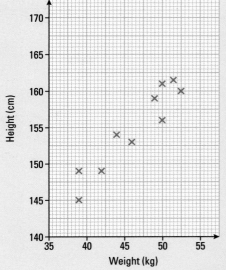

June 2008

9 A garage sells motorcycles.
The scatter graph shows information about the price and age of the motorcycles.

  a What type of correlation does the scatter graph show?

  b Draw a line of best fit on a copy of the scatter graph.

Mae buys a motorcycle from this garage for £1500.

  c Use your line of best fit to estimate the age of the motorcycle.

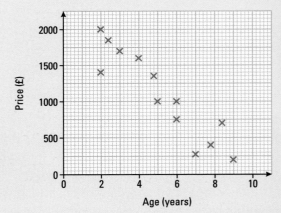

June 2007

10 The table gives the age and price of 10 second-hand Minis.

  a Estimate the approximate price of a new Mini.

  b Which Mini is different to the others? Suggest reasons why it is priced like it is.

Age (years)	Price
5	£5400
2	£7000
4	£5600
6	£3400
7	£5200
3	£6800
8	£1700
1	£10 500
8	£2000
6	£3200

A02

5 PROBABILITY

Weather forecasters use probability to predict the weather. The US Storm Prediction Center monitors all the storms in 'Tornado Alley' to predict which ones will become tornadoes. In 1925 the Tri-State Tornado, the longest and deadliest twister in US history, killed almost 700 people. At the time, it was thought that attempting to predict a tornado would only cause panic, so meteorologists were banned from studying tornadoes or even acknowledging their existence in public. Today better awareness and forecasting of tornadoes has reduced the average annual death toll to just 50.

◎ Objectives

In this chapter you will:
- ◎ learn to represent on a probability scale how likely it is that an event will happen
- ◎ learn to write probabilities as numbers
- ◎ solve problems involving fractions, decimals and percentages
- ◎ find probabilities from a sample space diagram
- ◎ discover how to estimate a probability from the results of an experiment
- ◎ find probabilities from a two-way table
- ◎ use ratios to solve problems.

◈ Before you start

You need to know:
- ◎ your tables and the rules of basic arithmetic
- ◎ how to use a number line
- ◎ how to add and subtract fractions and decimals.

5.1 The probability scale

◎ Objectives

- You can represent how likely it is that an event will happen on a probability scale.
- You can use words to describe probabilities.
- You can convert between fractions, decimals and percentages.

⬦ Why do this?

How likely is it that it will rain tomorrow? A knowledge of probability helps us to decide whether to wear a coat or not.

⬥ Get Ready

Will Christmas Day always follow Christmas Eve? Is it possible to throw a 7 on an ordinary dice?

The probability scale

Key Points

- An **event** that is **certain** to happen has a probability of 1.
- An event that is **impossible** happen has a probability of 0.
- The **probability** that an event will happen is always **less than or equal to** 1, or **greater than or equal to** 0. This can be written as $0 \leqslant$ probability $\leqslant 1$.

Fractions

Key Points

- A probability that lies between 0 and 1 can be expressed as a fraction or a decimal.
- A fraction such as $\frac{3}{4}$ is made up of a numerator and a denominator.
  The denominator tells you how many parts the whole is divided into, in this case 4.
  The numerator tells you how many of these parts you have, in this case 3.
- To convert a fraction into a decimal you divide the numerator by the denominator.

Example 1 — Convert $\frac{3}{4}$ into a decimal.

```
     0.7 5
4 ) 3.0 0
    2 8
    ‾‾‾
      2 0
      2 0
```

> An easier way of doing this is to divide 3 by 4 using a calculator.

Example 2 — Convert 0.88 to a fraction.

$$0.88 = \frac{88}{100} = \frac{22}{25}$$

> Using place value, 0.88 is 8 tenths and 8 hundredths. This is the same as 88 hundredths. Cancel to make the fraction in its simplest form.

Percentages

Key Points

- Percentage (%) means number of parts per hundred.
- To write fractions, decimals and percentages in order of size first convert them all to decimals.

Example 3   Convert 45% to a fraction and a decimal.

$45\% = \dfrac{45}{100} = 0.45$ ⟵ [Put the percentage over 100.]

[To change to a decimal drop the % sign and move the decimal point 2 places to the left.]

Example 4   Use a calculator to write these in order of size.

$0.46 \qquad \dfrac{5}{8} \qquad 33\% \qquad \dfrac{1}{4}$

0.46 is already a decimal

$\dfrac{5}{8} = 0.625$ ⟵ [5 ÷ 8 =]

$33\% = 0.33$

$\dfrac{1}{4} = 0.25$ ⟵ [1 ÷ 4 =]

In order of size $0.25, 0.33, 0.46, 0.625$.

Example 5   Represent how likely each of the following events is on a **probability scale**.

    a If today is Monday, tomorrow will be Tuesday.
    b A human will grow to be 10 metres tall.
    c It will be sunny every day for a week in January in London.
    d If you spin an ordinary coin it will land on a head.

[Draw a probability scale from 0 to 1.]

a
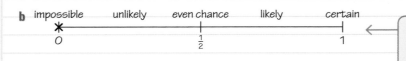
It is certain that the day after Monday will be Tuesday. For a certain event the probability = 1, so mark this with a cross (x) on the number line.

b
It is impossible for a human to grow to be 10 m tall. For an impossible event the probability = 0.

c
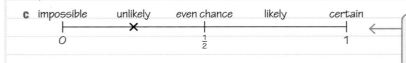
It is possible that it will be sunny every day for a week in January in London but it is unlikely.

d

You are just as likely to get a head as a tail. It is an even chance.

⚙ Exercise 5A

Questions in this chapter are targeted at the grades indicated.

F

1 How likely is each of the following events? In each case, represent your answer on a probability scale.

   a The sun will rise tomorrow.

   b A pet cat will live for ever.

   c The next baby born will be a girl.

   d You will use a mobile phone today.

   e It will snow on Christmas Day in Manchester.

2 Give two examples of events that you think:

   a are impossible

   b are certain

   c have about an even chance

   d are possible but unlikely

   e are likely.

3 If you take 7 letters at random from a bag of 100 letters, how likely is it that you will be able to use the letters to make a 7-letter word? Represent your answer on a probability scale.

4 How likely do you think it is that the next national election will be won by:

   a Conservatives

   b Labour

   c Liberal Democrats?

   Represent your answers on the same probability scale.

5 **a** Change the following to decimals: $\frac{1}{2}$, $\frac{4}{5}$, 25%, 36%.

   b Change the following to fractions: 0.3, 0.25, 35%, 62%.

   c Change the following to percentages: 0.55, 0.67, $\frac{1}{10}$, $\frac{3}{5}$.

6 Write the following in order, starting with the smallest: 0.2, 48%, $\frac{1}{10}$, $\frac{4}{5}$.

E

5.2 Writing probabilities as numbers

◎ Objective

- You can use a number to represent a probability.

❓ Why do this?

If you write probabilities as numbers it is easier to compare them to make a decision, for example which raffle prize you are more likely to win at a school fair.

◈ Get Ready

Copy and complete this table.

Fraction	$\frac{3}{10}$		$\frac{3}{8}$	
Decimal		0.6		
Percentage				65%

🔍 Key Points

- **Outcomes** are mutually exclusive when they cannot happen at the same time. For example, rolling a 3 and rolling a 4 on a dice are **mutually exclusive** outcomes – you cannot roll a 3 and a 4 at the same time.
- For **equally likely** outcomes the probability that an event will happen is

$$\text{Probability} = \frac{\text{number of successful outcomes}}{\text{total number of possible outcomes}}$$

- A probability can be written as a fraction, a decimal or a percentage.

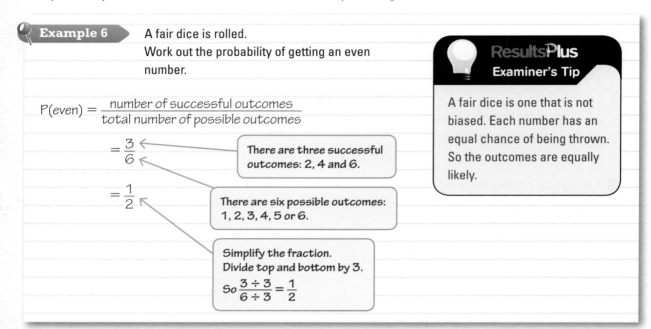

Example 6 A fair dice is rolled.
Work out the probability of getting an even number.

$$P(\text{even}) = \frac{\text{number of successful outcomes}}{\text{total number of possible outcomes}}$$

$$= \frac{3}{6}$$

There are three successful outcomes: 2, 4 and 6.

$$= \frac{1}{2}$$

There are six possible outcomes: 1, 2, 3, 4, 5 or 6.

Simplify the fraction.
Divide top and bottom by 3.
So $\frac{3 \div 3}{6 \div 3} = \frac{1}{2}$

ResultsPlus
Examiner's Tip

A fair dice is one that is not biased. Each number has an equal chance of being thrown. So the outcomes are equally likely.

⚙️ Exercise 5B

F

1 Here are a number of shapes.
One of these shapes is chosen at random. Work out the probability that the shape will be:

   a a square   **b** a triangle   **c** a square or a triangle.

2 A game consists of spinning a pointer on a dial.
Work out the probability that the pointer will stop on

   a 0   **b** 1   **c** 2   **d** 3

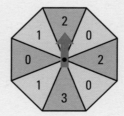

3 A bag contains 10 counters. 3 of the counters are red and 7 of the counters are blue.
A counter is taken at random from the bag. Write down the probability that it will be:

   a red   **b** blue   **c** yellow.

F

E

4 A letter is chosen at random from the word STATISTICS. Write down the probability that it will be:
   a A   b S   c I   d S or T   e G.

5 A fair dice is rolled. Work out the probability of getting:
   a a 5   b a 1 or a 2   c an odd number
   d a number less than 5   e a number greater than 6 f a prime number.

6 There are 120 raffle tickets in a hat. Of these, 67 are yellow and the rest are green.
   A raffle ticket is taken at random from the hat. Work out the probability that it will be:
   a yellow   b green.

7 A box of sweets contains 3 mints, 7 toffees and 5 lemon drops.
   A sweet is taken at random from the box. Write down the probability that it will be:
   a a mint   b a toffee   c a lemon drop
   d a mint or a toffee   e not a toffee   f not a lemon drop or a toffee.

5.3 The probability that something will *not* happen

◎ Objective

◎ You can work out the probability that something will not happen if you know the probability that it will happen.

◈ Why do this?

You could work out the probability of not being hit by lightning, because there is a known probability for the chance of being hit by lightning.

◈ Get Ready

Can you find the missing numbers?

a $1 - 0.7 = ?$ b $1 - ? = 0.6$ c $1 - \frac{1}{2} = ?$ d $1 - ? = \frac{3}{4}$

🕐 Key Point

◉ If the probability of an event happening is P then the probability of it not happening is $1 - P$.

◉ If two events, A and B, cannot happen at the same time, the probability of one or the other happening is given by P(A) + P(B). This can be extended to three or more events.

◉ If a set of events contains all **possible** outcomes, then the sum of their probabilities must come to 1. $\Sigma p = 1$

Example 7   The probability that it will rain tomorrow is 0.2.
                Work out the probability that it will not rain tomorrow.

P(not rain) = 1 − P(rain)
            = 1 − 0.2   ⟵   If the probability that it will rain tomorrow is 0.2,
            = 0.8   then the probability it will not rain is 1 − 0.2.

E

Exercise 5C

1   The probability that it will snow on New Year's Day is 0.3.
    Work out the probability that it will not snow on New Year's Day.

2   The probability that my bike will get a puncture on the way to school today is 0.15.
    Work out the probability that my bike will not get a puncture on the way to school today.

3   The probability that Stephanie will have chips for dinner tonight is $\frac{2}{3}$.
    Work out the probability that Stephanie will not have chips tonight.

4   The probability that my lottery ticket will win a prize is $\frac{3}{53}$.
    Work out the probability that my lottery ticket will not win a prize.

5   A weather forecaster says that there is a 70% chance of getting rain tomorrow.
    What is the probability that it will not rain tomorrow?

6   The probability that Tracy will not eat all her carrots at lunch is 0.64.
    Work out the probability that she will eat all her carrots at lunch.

7   An insurance broker says that when she receives a claim the probability that it will not be for an accident in the home is 0.325. Work out the probability that the next claim received by the insurance broker will be for an accident in the home.

8   The probability that Kimberley's train will be late is 0.32. Kimberley says that the probability that her train will not be late is 0.78. She is wrong. Explain why.

Example 8

The diagram shows a 4-sided spinner that is biased.
The spinner is spun.
This table gives the probability that it will land on B, C or D.

	A	B	C	D
Probability		0.13	0.45	0.25

Work out the probability that the spinner will land on A.

P(A) + 0.13 + 0.45 + 0.25 = 1 ←— It is certain that the spinner will land on A or B or C or D. So the probabilities add up to 1.

P(A) + 0.83 = 1 ←— Add the decimals: 0.13 + 0.45 + 0.25 = 0.83

P(A) = 1 − 0.83
     = 0.17 ←— Take 0.83 from both sides of the equation.

D

⚙ Exercise 5D

1 Heather's bus can either be early, on time or late.
This table gives the probability that her bus will be early and the probability that her bus will be late.

	early	on time	late
Probability	0.1		0.6

Work out the probability that Heather's bus will be on time.

2 A biased dice is rolled.
This table gives the probability that it will land on each of the numbers 1, 2, 3, 4 and 5.

	1	2	3	4	5	6
Probability	0.2	0.1	0.3	0.2	0.1	

Work out the probability that the dice will land on 6.

3 Imran has some coloured cards. Each card is either red or yellow or blue or green. One of these cards is taken at random. This table gives the probability that the card will be red or blue or green.

Colour	red	yellow	blue	green
Probability	0.36		0.19	0.28

Work out the probability that the card will:

a be yellow

b not be blue

c be a red card or a green card.

4 A bag contains a number of balls. Each ball is either red or blue or yellow or green.
A ball is taken at random from the bag.

The probability that the ball will be red is 0.25.
The probability that the ball will be blue is 0.3.
The probability that the ball will be yellow is 0.2.
Work out the probability that the ball will be green.

5 When Kasha spins this 3-sided spinner, the probability that it will land on 1 is $\frac{2}{9}$.
The probability that it will land on 3 is $\frac{4}{9}$.
Work out the probability that it will land on 2.

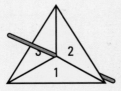

6 When Weymouth Wanderers play football they can win, lose or draw the game.
The probability that they will win the game is $\frac{3}{5}$. The probability that they will lose the game is $\frac{3}{10}$.
Work out the probability that they will draw the game.

5.4 Using fractions, decimals and percentages in problems

Objectives

- You calculate a fraction of a quantity.
- You find a percentage of a quantity.
- You use decimals to find quantities.
- You understand the multiplicative nature of percentages as operators.

Why do this?

You have a token that gives you 20% off the price of a book. Because there is a sale on you are given another 10% off the book.
Do you get 30% off the book?

Get Ready

Convert these decimals and percentages to fractions in their simplest form:

1. a 0.25   b 0.6
2. a 75%   b 35%

Finding a fraction of an amount

Example 9   Work out

$\quad$ a $\frac{1}{9}$ of 54   b $\frac{5}{9}$ of 54

a $\frac{1}{9}$ of $54 = \frac{1}{9} \times \frac{54}{1} = 54 \div 9 = 6$

b $\frac{5}{9}$ of $54 = 5 \times \frac{1}{9}$ of $54 = 5 \times 6 = 30$

Finding a percentage of a quantity

Key Points

- To find a percentage of a quantity write the percentage as a fraction and then multiply the quantity by the fraction.

Example 10   An article that costs £50 is in a sale with 15% off this amount.
Work out the price.

$15\% = \frac{15}{100}$ ← Write the percentage as a fraction.

$\frac{1}{100}$ of £50 = £0.5 ← Divide by the denominator to find 1% of the price.

$\frac{15}{100}$ of £50 = $15 \times \frac{1}{100}$ of £50 = $15 \times £0.5 = £7.50$ ← Multiply by the numerator to find 15% of the price.

£50 – £7.50 = £42.50 ← Subtract this amount from the original price to find the sale price.

Example 11 You have a token that gives you 20% off the price of a book. Because there is a sale on you are given a further 10% off a book. The book costs £20 before deductions. Work out the amount you would have to pay for the book.

$$20\% \text{ of } £20 = \frac{£20}{100} \times 20 \qquad \leftarrow \boxed{\text{Work out 20\%.}}$$

$$= £0.20 \times 20$$
$$= £4.00$$

After 20% reduction price is £20 − £4 = £16 $\leftarrow \boxed{\text{Take 20\% from the price.}}$

$$10\% \text{ of } £16 = \frac{£16}{100} \times 10 \qquad \leftarrow \boxed{\begin{array}{l}\text{Work out 10\% of}\\\text{the new price.}\end{array}}$$

$$= £0.16 \times 10$$
$$= £1.60$$

After further 10% reduction the price is £16 − £1.60 = £14.40. $\leftarrow \boxed{\begin{array}{l}\text{Subtract from the new}\\\text{price to give the answer.}\end{array}}$

Finding one quantity as a percentage of another

Key Points

◉ To find one quantity as a percentage of another, write down the first quantity as a fraction of the second quantity.

Example 12 Write down 18 out of 20 as a percentage.

$$18 \text{ out of } 20 = \frac{18}{20} = \frac{9}{10} = \frac{90}{100} = 90\%$$

Exercise 5E

1. Alice gets a mark of 34 out of 40 in a test. Work out what this is as a percentage.

2. A computer has a price tag of £300. In the sale there is a 20% reduction. What is the sale price?

3. The manufacturer of a camera charges a shop £90. The shopkeeper then adds 25% to this price before he puts it for sale in his shop. Work out the shop price.

4. Mr. Hartop borrows £1200 from the bank for one year in order to buy a new washing machine. The bank charges him interest of 18% per year. How much does he have to pay back to the bank?

* 5. Dacksons have a sale on. There is to be 20% off everything. On the last day they advertise that there will be a further 10% off.
Jack says ' This CD costs £10, so I will pay £7.'
The shopkeeper says the cost will be £7.20.
Explain why Jack and the shopkeeper reached different prices.

E

D

C

5.5 Sample space diagrams

◉ Objective

● You can record all the possible outcomes of an experiment in a sample space diagram.

⟲ Why do this?

When two things happen at the same time a sample space diagram is s good way to show all the possible outcomes.

⬆ Get Ready

Write down all the possible outcomes when you:

a spin a coin   **b** roll a dice   **c** play a game of football

◗ Key Point

● A **sample space diagram** can be used to find a **theoretical probability**.

Example 13   An ordinary dice is rolled and a 4-sided spinner is spun.

a Draw a sample space diagram to show all the possible outcomes.

b Work out the probability of getting a total score of 7.

a

Spinner	4	(1, 4)	(2, 4)	(3, 4)	(4, 4)	(5, 4)	(6, 4)
	3	(1, 3)	(2, 3)	(3, 3)	(4, 3)	(5, 3)	(6, 3)
	2	(1, 2)	(2, 2)	(3, 2)	(4, 2)	(5, 2)	(6, 2)
	1	(1, 1)	(2, 1)	(3, 1)	(4, 1)	(5, 1)	(6, 1)
		1	2	3	4	5	6

Dice

> A sample space diagram shows all the possible outcomes, e.g. (6, 4) is the outcome of rolling a 6 on the dice and spinning a 4 on the spinner.

b $P(7) = \dfrac{\text{number of successful outcomes}}{\text{total number of possible outcomes}}$

> Identify all the possible ways of getting a total score of 7: (3, 4), (4, 3), (5, 2) and (6, 1).

$= \dfrac{4}{24}$

> There are four outcomes which give a total score of 7.

$= \dfrac{1}{6}$

> There are a total of 24 possible outcomes.

> This is the theoretical probability. The probability you expect to get for a fair dice and a fair spinner.

Exercise 5F

1   A coin is spun, and an ordinary dice is rolled. Show all the possible outcomes.

2   An ordinary dice is rolled and a 4-sided spinner is spun.
    Use the sample space diagram in Example 12 to work out the probability of getting:
    a   a total score of 4
    b   the same number on the dice and the spinner
    c   a total score less than 6.

3   The ace, king, queen and jack of clubs and the ace, king, queen and jack of diamonds are put into two
    piles. The sample space diagram shows all the possible outcomes when a card is taken from each pile.

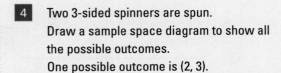

	J	AJ	KJ	QJ	JJ
Clubs	Q	AQ	KQ	QQ	JQ
	K	AK	KK	QK	JK
	A	AA	KA	QA	JA
		A	K	Q	J
			Diamonds		

Work out the probability that:
a   both cards will be aces
b   the cards will be a pair
c   only one of the cards will be a jack
d   at least one card will be a king
e   one card will be diamond
f   neither card will be a queen
g   both cards will be diamonds.

4   Two 3-sided spinners are spun.
    Draw a sample space diagram to show all
    the possible outcomes.
    One possible outcome is (2, 3).

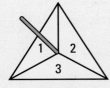

Spinner 1   Spinner 2

5   Mandy has some sheets and pillowcases in a drawer. The colours of the sheets are either white or
    yellow or blue or green. The colours of pillowcases are either white or green or orange. Mandy takes at
    random a sheet and a pillowcase from the drawer.
    a   Draw a sample space diagram to show all the possible combinations of colours for the sheets and
        pillowcases.
    b   Work out the probability that Mandy takes a sheet and a pillowcase of:
        i   the same colour   ii   different colours.

6   Simon is going to spin a 3-sided spinner and a 4-sided
    spinner. The spinners are fair.
    What is the most likely total score.
    Give a reason for your answer.

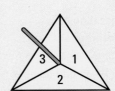
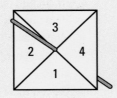

117

5.6 Relative frequency

Objectives

- You can find an estimate of a probability from the results of an experiment.
- You can compare experimental and theoretical probabilities.

Why do this?

Insurance companies use relative frequency to estimate risk. The greater the number of claims the greater the risk.

Get Ready

Simplify these fractions.

a $\frac{2}{4}$　　　b $\frac{6}{9}$　　　c $\frac{8}{12}$　　　d $\frac{50}{100}$

Key Points

- You can use **relative frequency** to find an estimate for a probability.
- Estimated probability $= \dfrac{\text{number of successful trials}}{\text{total number of trials}}$
- The estimated probability may be different from the theoretical probability.
- Generally the more **trials** you undertake the nearer your estimate will be to the actual probability.

Example 14

Samina spins a fair coin 50 times.
She gets 21 heads.
Write down the estimated and theoretical probability of getting a head.

ResultsPlus
Examiner's Tip

The estimated probability may be different from the theoretical probability.

Estimated probability $= \dfrac{\text{number of successful trials}}{\text{total number of trials}} = \dfrac{21}{50}$

Theoretical probability $= \dfrac{1}{2}$

Exercise 5G

E

1　Roll a dice 60 times and record your results in a frequency table like this.

a Use the results in your table to work out the estimated probability of getting:

　i a 6
　ii an odd number
　iii a number bigger than 4.

b Write down the theoretical probability of getting:

　i a 6　　　　ii an odd number　　　iii a number bigger than 4.

c Do you think your dice is fair? Give a reason for your answer.

Number	Tally	Frequency
1		
2		
3		
4		
5		
6		
	Total	**60**

E

2 **a** Write down the theoretical probability of getting a head when you spin an ordinary coin.

 b Now spin a coin 50 times and record your results in a frequency table.

 c Use your results to write down the estimated probability of getting a head. Comment on your answer.

3 Throw a drawing pin 50 times and record whether it lands on its head or on its side.

 a Use your results to write down the estimated probability of getting a head.

 b How could you improve on your answer to part **a**?

Head   Side

4 Make a 4-sided dice of your own out of card.
 Test the dice to see whether it is fair or not.

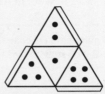

Net of a 4-sided dice

5 A letter is chosen at random from the words in a book.

 a Work out an estimate of the probability of getting the letter k.

 b Is your estimate affected by the language in which the book is written? Explain your answer.

A02
A03

5.7 **Two-way tables**

◎ Objective

○ You can find probabilities from a two-way table.

⦾ Why do this?

Two-way tables help travel agents decide where people are most likely to go on holiday at certain times of the year. For example, beach holidays are more popular in the summer and ski holidays are more popular in winter.

◈ Get Ready

Can you find the missing numbers?
a $3 + 4 + ? = 10$
b $9 + ? + 11 = 25$
c $? + 16 + 9 = 35$

🔑 Key Points

◉ For a two-way table, sum of row totals = sum of column totals.

Example 15　Carmen asks 20 people where they went for their summer holidays.
This two-way table gives some of the information from her results.

	France	Italy	Spain	Total
Boys	4	5		11
Girls	1			9
Total		7		20

a Copy and complete the table.

b Carmen picks one of the 20 students at random.
Write down the probability that this student:

　i will be a girl　　　ii went to Italy　　　iii will be a girl who went to France.

a

This number is 6 because:
$1 + 2 + 6 = 9$

This number is 2 because
$4 + 5 + 2 = 11$

	France	Italy	Spain	Total
Boys	4	5	2	11
Girls	1	2	6	9
Total	5	7	8	20

This number is 9 because
$11 + 9 = 20$

This number is 5 because:
$4 + 1 = 5$

This number is 2 because:
$5 + 2 = 7$

This number is 8 because
$2 + 6 = 8$ or $5 + 7 + 8 = 20$

b　i From the table above, it can be seen that 9 students are girls.
So, $P(\text{girl}) = \frac{9}{20}$

Use $P = \dfrac{\text{number of successful outcomes}}{\text{total number of possible outcomes}}$

Here 9 students are girls, so the number of successful outcomes = 9.
There are 20 students altogether, so the total number of possible outcomes = 20.

　ii The table shows that 7 students went to Italy.
So, $P(\text{Italy}) = \frac{7}{20}$

　iii From the table, it can be seen that 1 girl
went to France. So, $P(\text{girl, France}) = \frac{1}{20}$

Exercise 5H

D

1　Kumar counted the number of butterflies and the number of moths in his garden in May and June.
The following two-way table provides some of the information from his results.

	Butterflies	Moths	Total
May	9	4	
June			
Total		7	25

Copy and complete the table.

2 The table below gives some information about how some students travel to school.

	Walk	Bus	Cycle	Total
Boys	4		3	12
Girls	7			
Total		9		25

a Copy and complete the table.

b One of the students is picked at random. Work out the probability that this student is:
- **i** a girl
- **ii** a girl who walks to school
- **iii** a boy who cycles to school
- **iv** a student who comes by bus.

3 45 students each went to one activity on Saturday night.
The following two-way table shows some information about where they went.

	Cinema	Club	Bowling	Total
Boys	5			23
Girls			4	
Total	14	15		45

a Copy and complete the table.

b One of the students is picked at random. Write down the probability that this student:
- **i** will be a boy
- **ii** went to the cinema
- **iii** will be a girl who went bowling.

4 Some students each had one drink and one snack in the school canteen.
The table below gives some information about what the students had to eat and drink.

	Orange	Lemonade	Milk	Total
Sandwiches	5			13
Biscuits	4		5	
Crisps			1	16
Total	17	18	7	

a Copy and complete the table.

b One of the students is picked at random.
Use your table to write down the probability that this student had:
- **i** lemonade
- **ii** crisps
- **iii** orange and biscuits
- **iv** lemonade and biscuits.

c John says that the probability of picking someone who had milk and biscuits is the same as picking someone who had orange and sandwiches. Is he right? Give a reason for your answer.

5.8 Predicting outcomes

⬆ **Get Ready**

Kim spins this fair spinner 100 times.
How many times would you expect it to land on a 3?

🌑 **Key Points**

◎ Predicted number of outcomes = probability × number of trials

🔍 **Example 16** ▶ A fair 4-sided spinner is spun 100 times.
Find an estimate for the number of times it will land on a 3.

The theoretical probability that the spinner will land on a 3 is $\frac{1}{4}$.

> Use P(3) = …
> Here there is one outcome which is successful (i.e. '3'), and the total number of possible outcomes = 4 (i.e. 1, 2, 3 or 4).

So, when the spinner is spun 100 times we expect it to land on a 3.

$\frac{1}{4} \times 100 = 25$ times.

> Predicted number of outcomes = probability × number of trials
> $\frac{1}{4} \times 100 = 100 \div 4 = 25$

⚙ **Exercise 5I**

E

1 An ordinary coin is spun 100 times. How many times do you expect it to land on a head?

2 Piers spins an ordinary 5-sided spinner (numbered 1 to 5) 150 times.
How many times can he expect it to land on a 4?

3 Harry is going to roll an ordinary dice 90 times. Work out an estimate for the number of times it will land on:
  a 6 **b** an even number **c** 1 or 2.

4 The table gives information about the probability that Tom will win, draw or lose a game of Go.

	Win	Draw	Lose
Probability	0.4	0.25	0.35

Tom is going to play 40 games of Go.
Find an estimate for the number of games he will:

a win

b lose.

5 A bag contains 3 red balls and 5 blue balls.
A ball is taken at random from the bag and its colour is recorded. The ball is now put back into the bag and another ball is taken at random from the bag. This is repeated 60 times.
Find an estimate for the total number of:

a red balls taken from the bag

b blue balls taken from the bag.

6 The probability that an insurance company will get a claim for an accident in the home is 0.72.
If the insurance company gets 340 claims during the next month, find an estimate for the number of these claims that will not be for an accident in the home.

*__**7**__ The diagram shows part of Holly's design for a game. In her game a player pays x pence to spin a star. When the star stops spinning the player wins the amount shown by the arrow.
Holly wants to gain an average of 5p each time the game is played.
Show how this can be done by adding six more numbers to the star and finding a suitable value for x.

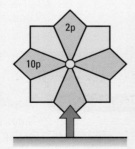

5.9 **Ratio and proportion**

◎ **Objectives**

- ○ You can use ratios.
- ○ You can write ratios in their simplest form.
- ○ You can divide a quantity in a given ratio.
- ○ You can solve a ratio problem in context.

◈ **Why do this?**

You want to mix petrol and oil to make a mixture suitable for a two-stroke engine. The amount of petrol to oil is given as a ratio.

◈ **Get Ready**

1. Write $\frac{3}{12}$ in its simplest form.
2. Write $\frac{40}{100}$ in its simplest form.

Key Points

⊙ **Ratio** is the quantity of one thing compared to the quantity of something else.

⊙ A ratio of 1 part oil to 20 parts of petrol would be written as 1 : 20.

⊙ If you borrow money using a credit card you have to pay **interest** on the money you borrow. The more money you borrow the more interest you have to pay.
If you borrow £10 and you pay £0.60 in interest then if you borrow £20 you would pay twice as much i.e. £1.20. The interest you pay is proportional to the amount you borrow.

Example 17   For every 10 red cars sold by a garage they sell 6 silver cars and 8 blue ones.
Write down the ratio of the number of red cars to the number of silver cars to the number of blue cars.

The ratio is $10 : 6 : 8$ ←   10, 6 and 8 are divisible by 2

$= 5 : 3 : 4$ in the simplest form.   ←   5, 3 and 4 are not divisible by any other number so this is the simplest form.

Example 18   The ratio of games won, lost and drawn by a team was $2 : 3 : 5$.
What fraction of the games did the team lose?

$2 + 3 + 5 = 10$ games in total

For every 10 games, 2 are won, 3 are lost and 5 are drawn.

$\frac{3}{10}$ of the games were lost.

Example 19   Jordan, Sam and Owen share a total of £52 pocket money per month in the ratio of their ages which is $6 : 8 : 12$.
Work out how much each boy gets.

$6 + 8 + 12 = 26$

$\frac{£52}{26} = £2$

$£2 \times 6 = £12$, so Jordan gets £12 per month.
$£2 \times 8 = £16$, so Sam gets £16 per month.
$£2 \times 12 = £24$, so Owen gets £24 per month.

Example 20   Courtney buys 3 tins of soup for £1.95. Imogen buys 5 tins of soup.
Work out how much Imogen pays for her 5 tins.

$\frac{1.95}{3} = £0.65$ ←   Find the cost of one tin.

$5 \times £0.65 = £3.25$ ←   Multiply the cost of 1 tin by 5.

Exercise 5J

1   Thames United played 24 matches. They won 7, lost 6 and drew the rest.
    Write the matches won, lost and drawn as a ratio.

2   In a car park there are 30 white cars, 25 red cars and 45 silver cars.
    Write down the ratio of the number of white cars to red cars to silver cars in its simplest form.

3   In a call centre there are 140 workers. The ratio of supervisors to workers is 1 : 9.
    Write down the number of supervisors.

4   Megan makes up a drink. It is made of orange juice and lemonade in the ratio 1 : 4.
    She makes 10 litres of the drink. How much orange juice will she need?

5   The cost of five jars of coffee is £12.75.
    Work out the cost of seven jars of coffee.

6   Nathan is 10 years old. Shannon is 14 years old. They are to share £120 in the ratio of their ages. Work
    out how much each will get.

7   Here is a list of the ingredients to make 15 shortbread biscuits.
    110 g butter   50 g sugar   175 g flour
    Jasmine is going to make 60 shortbread biscuits for a cake sale. How much of each ingredient will she need?

8   In a bag of sweets the ratio of red to yellow to green sweets is 2 : 3 : 5.
    a What fraction of the sweets is red?
    Yosef picks a sweet out of the bag.
    b What is the probability that it is a yellow sweet?

E

D

C

Chapter review

◉ An **event** that is **certain** to happen has a probability of 1.

◉ An event that is **impossible** has a probability of 0.

◉ The **probability** that an event will happen is always **less than or equal to** 1, or **greater than or equal** to 0.
   This can be written as $0 \leqslant$ probability $\leqslant 1$.

◉ **Outcomes** are **mutually exclusive** when they cannot happen at the same time.

◉ For **equally likely** outcomes the probability that an event will happen is

   $$\text{Probability} = \frac{\text{number of successful outcomes}}{\text{total number of possible outcomes}}$$

◉ A probability can be written as a fraction, a decimal or a percentage.

◉ If the probability of an event happening is p then the probability of it not happening is $1 - p$.

◉ You can list all **possible** outcomes of an experiment in a **sample space diagram**.

◉ You can use **relative frequency** to find an estimate for a probability.

◉ Estimated probability $= \dfrac{\text{number of successful trials}}{\text{total number of trials}}$

◉ For a two-way table, sum of row totals = sum of column totals.

◉ Predicted number of outcomes = probability × number of **trials**.

Review exercise

G

1 Tom throws an ordinary coin once.

  a On a copy of the probability scale, mark with a cross (×) the probability that the coin will show tails.

Tom rolls an ordinary dice once.

  b On a copy of the probability scale, mark with a cross (×) the probability that he will score a number less than 6.

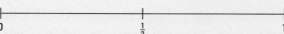

Tom takes a Maths test.

  c On a copy of the probability scale, mark with a cross (×) the probability that he will score more than 0.

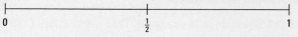

Nov 2008

F

2 Lucy uses some letter cards to spell the word "NOVEMBER".

Lucy takes one of these cards as random.
Write down the probability that Lucy takes a card with a letter E.

Nov 2009

3 Here are some statements.
On a copy, draw an arrow from each statement to the word which best describes its likelihood.
One has been done for you.

| A head is obtained when a fair coin is thrown once. |
| A number less than 7 will be scored when an ordinary six-sided dice is rolled once. |
| It will rain every day for a week next July in London. |
| A red disc is obtained when a disc is taken at random from a bag containing 9 red discs and 2 blue discs. |

| Certain |
| Likely |
| Even |
| Unlikely |
| Impossible |

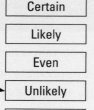

June 2008

4 Iqbal eats in a cafe.
He can choose **one** main course and **one** piece of fruit.

Main Course	Fruit
Fish	*Apple*
Lamb	*Banana*
Salad	*Pear*

One possible combination is (Fish, Pear).
Write down all the possible combinations that Iqbal can choose.

March 2008

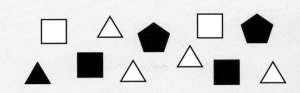

5 The diagram shows some 3-sided, 4-sided and 5-sided shapes.

The shapes are black or white.

a Copy and complete the two-way table.

	Black	White	Total
3-sided shape		4	5
4-sided shape	2		
5-sided shape		0	
Total			11

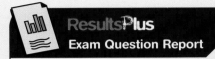

92% of students did very well on part **a** of this question.

Ed takes a shape at random.

b Write down the probability the shape is white **and** 3-sided.

March 2008

6 Ishah spins a fair 5-sided spinner.

She then throws a fair coin.

a List all the possible outcomes she could get.

Ishah spins the spinner once and throws the coin once.

b Work out the probability that she will get a 1 and a head.

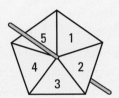

March 2009 adapted

7 80 children went on a school trip.

They went to London or to York.

23 boys and 19 girls went to London.

14 boys went to York.

a Use this information to complete a copy of the two-way table.

	London	York	Total
Boys			
Girls			
Total			

One of these 80 children is chosen at random.

b What is the probability that this child went to London?

March 2009

8 There are three beads in a bag.

One bead is blue, one bead is yellow and one bead is green.

Zoe takes a bead at random from the bag.

a On a copy of the probability scale, mark with the letter B the probability that she takes a blue bead.

Zoe now throws a coin.

One possible outcome for the bead and the coin is (green, heads).

b List all the possible outcomes for the bead and the coin.

One has already been done for you.

May 2008

E

9 There are 3 red pens, 4 blue pens and 5 black pens in a box.
Sameena takes a pen, at random, from the box.
Write down the probability that she takes a black pen.

June 2008

10 There are 8 pencils in a pencil case.

1 pencil is red.
4 pencils are blue.
The rest are black.

A pencil is taken at random from the pencil case.
Write down the probability that the pencil is black.

June 2008

11 Emily has a bag of 20 fruit flavour sweets.

7 of the sweets are strawberry flavour,
11 are lime flavour,
2 are lemon flavour.

Emily takes at random a sweet from the bag.
Write down the probability that Emily

a takes a strawberry flavour sweet

b does **not** take a lime flavour sweet

c takes an orange flavour sweet.

June 2006

D

12 A bag contains only red, green and blue counters.
The table shows the probability that a counter chosen at random from the bag will be red or will be green.

Colour	Red	Green	Blue
Probability	0.5	0.3	

Mary takes a counter at random from the bag.
a Work out the probability that Mary takes a blue counter.
The bag contains 50 counters.
b Work out how many green counters there are in the bag.

March 2009

13 Here is a 5-sided spinner.
The sides of the spinner are labelled 1, 2, 3, 4 and 5
The spinner is biased.
The probability that the spinner will land on each of the numbers
1, 2, 3 and 4 is given in the table.

Number	1	2	3	4	5
Probability	0.15	0.05	0.2	0.25	x

Work out the value of x.

Nov 2008

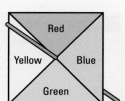

14 Here is a 4-sided spinner.

The sides of the spinner are labelled Red, Blue, Green and Yellow.

The spinner is biased.

The table shows the probability that the spinner will land on each of the colours Red, Yellow and Green.

Colour	Red	Blue	Green	Yellow
Probability	0.2		0.3	0.1

Work out the probability the spinner will land on Blue.   *May 2008*

15 Marco has a 4-sided spinner.

The sides of the spinner are numbered 1, 2, 3 and 4.

The spinner is biased.

The table shows the probability that the spinner will land on each of the numbers 1, 2 and 3.

Number	1	2	3	4
Probability	0.20	0.35	0.20	

a Work out the probability that the spinner will land on the number 4.

Marco spins the spinner 100 times.

b Work out an estimate for the number of times the spinner will land on the number 2.

16 Here are the ages, in years, of 15 teachers.

35 52 42 27 36 23 31 41 50 34 44 28 45 53

One of these teachers is picked at random.

Work out the probability that the teacher is more than 40 years old.   *May 2008 adapted*

17 Katie wants to buy a car. She decides to borrow £3500 from her father.

She adds interest of 3.5% to the loan and this total is the amount she must repay her father.

How much will Katie pay back to her father in total?

* 18 Rashida wishes to invest £2000 in a building society account for one year

The Internet offers two suggestions.

Dunstan Building Society

4% per annum
Paid yearly by cheque

Chestman Building Society

£3.50 per month
Plus
1% bonus at the end of the year

Which of these two investments gives Rashida the greatest return?

19 Blackcurrant ice cream uses the ingredients blackcurrants, cream, sugar and milk in the ratio 9 : 6 : 4 : 3.

Lena is going to make blackcurrant ice cream for the summer fete.

Each portion will have 150g of ice cream.

She has plenty of cream, milk and sugar in her store cupboard.

She picks 1.8 kilograms of blackcurrants.

a Work out how many full portions of ice cream Lena can make.

At the fete Lewis buys 3 portions of the blackcurrant ice cream for £3.36.

Nicole buys 5 portions of ice cream. There is a 10% discount if you buy 5 or more portions.

b Work out how much Nicole pays for the ice cream.

C A03

20 Two spinners are each numbered 1 to 4.

When they are both spun, the score is found by adding the two numbers.

E.g. a 1 and a 4 scores 5.

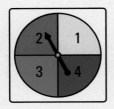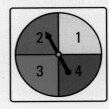

Three friends are playing with these spinners and devise
a set of rules.

If Alice gets a score of 6, 7 or 8 she wins.

If Robbie scores 4 or 5 he wins.

If Megan scores 1, 2 or 3 she wins.

Who should win the most games?

A03

21 You need two coins to play this game. Toss the coins and record the results.

If you get two heads the red horse moves one space.

If you get two tails the blue horse moves one space.

If you get a head and a tail then the yellow horse moves one space.

The first horse to move eight spaces wins the race.

Play the game three times and record your results.

Compare your results with a partner.

Can you explain why one horse has more of a chance than the others?

* **22** You need two dice to play this game.

Roll the dice and add up the numbers that are showing on the dice.

If you roll a 4 and a 5 then Horse 9 would move one space.

The first horse to move eight spaces is the winner.

Horse 1							
Horse 2							
Horse 3							
Horse 4							
Horse 5							
Horse 6							
Horse 7							
Horse 8							
Horse 9							
Horse 10							
Horse 11							
Horse 12							

One horse has no chance of winning. Can you state which one it is and why?

Play the game twice and describe the results of the race.

Compare your results with a partner.

Use probability to explain what is happening.

* **23** Devise and carry out an experiment to estimate the number of times a drawing pin would land pin up if you threw it 1000 times.

INTERPRETING AND DISPLAYING DATA

The following question helps you develop both your ability to select and apply a method (AO2) and your ability to solve problems using your skills of interpretation and proof (AO3). The AO2 skills come into parts (a) to (c) as, to find your estimates, you could either use a scatter graph with a line of best fit or put the values in order and estimate numerically. The AO3 elements come into part (d) where you are asked to comment on the reliability of your estimates.

Example The table below shows the reading speed and IQ of 10 students.

Reading speed (words per minute)	130	125	131	285	95	187	235	165	123	145
IQ	100	85	135	135	90	120	130	110	98	95

Use this information to estimate

a The reading speed of a student with an IQ of 120.

b The IQ of a student with a reading speed of 230.

c The reading speed of a student with an IQ of 80.

d Comment on the reliability of your answers.

Solution

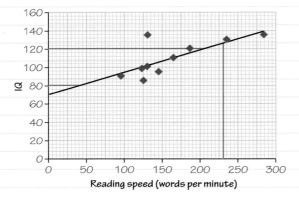

Drawing a scatter graph will help with this question.

Draw lines to show where you are reading off from your scatter graph. It shows the examiner how you are making your estimates.

a 205

b 126

c 40

d The scatter graph shows that there is positive correlation between IQ and reading speed. A line of best fit can be drawn. The answers to parts **a** and **b** are reasonably reliable as they lie within the range of the data. Part **c**, however, lies outside the data, so the estimate is unreliable.

1 The table below shows the predictions made for the highest temperature each day in Oxford.

Day	Monday	Tuesday	Wednesday	Thursday	Friday	Saturday	Sunday
Temperature °C	6	7	6	7	8	10	7

Use a suitable graph or chart to display this information.

2 The table below shows the amount of money a local council is investing in services.

Services	Roads & Transport	Education	Housing	Other
Amount of money (£million)	16	14	30	12

Use a suitable graph or chart to display this information in the annual report.

3 The table below shows the price of a book and the number of pages it contains.

Number of Pages	100	145	150	75	140	200	90	180
Cost of book	£5	£6.50	£7	£3.00	£6.50	£9	£4	£9.50

Use this information to estimate

a The cost of a book with 160 pages.

b The number of pages in a book costing £5.

c The cost of a book with 50 pages.

d Comment on the reliability of your answers.

4 Mr Smith and Miss Khan predict the positions of 8 swimmers in a race.

Actual	1	2	3	4	5	6	7	8
Mr Smith	6	3	4	2	5	1	8	7
Miss Khan	3	1	2	4	6	7	5	8

Which teacher is closest to predicting the actual positions?

The following question helps you develop both your ability to select and apply a method (AO2) and your ability to solve problems using your skills of interpretation and proof (AO3). The AO2 skills come into part (a) as there is more than one way to compare the players so you will need to choose a method. Your AO3 skills are needed in part (c) as you will need to work through several steps to solve this problem. There are also some functional elements as average performance over a number of competitions is often used to decide places on teams in sport.

Example   The table below shows the number of runs scored by cricketers over a number of matches.

	Runs scored in 10 matches									
Jones	42	0	19	49	72	29	31	22	16	20
Phillips	68	14	64	24	18	4	5	64	32	32
Bakir	18	24	35	9	2	0	8			76
Aziz	30	31	29	28	32	34	25	35	29	30

Bakir did not play in all of the matches.

a   Compare and contrast the players' scores.

b   Cooke's mean score over 3 matches was 42.

   Write down 3 scores which could have given him this mean.

   Smith played in the first 9 matches and scored a mean of 30 runs.

c   How many runs does he need to score in the final match to give him a better average than the players in the table?

Solution   a

	Mean	Range
Jones	30	72
Phillips	32.5	64
Bakir	21.5	76
Aziz	30.3	10

> Compare the mean and range for each player.

Bakir has the lowest mean average (21.5) and he is the least consistent player with a range of 76.
Aziz is the most consistent player with a range of 10 but he never gets a really high score.
Phillips has the highest mean score (32.5) and he is more consistent than Jones and Bakir.
Jones has the second lowest mean average and he isn't very consistent.

b   Cooke's average was 42. He scored a different number of runs in each match.
Total score over 3 matches is $3 \times 42 = 126$
Scores could be 41, 42 and 43.

c   In 9 matches Smith scores $9 \times 30 = 270$ runs.
The best average so far is Phillips' (32.5).
In 10 matches an average of $32.5 = 325$ runs

> Find the total number of runs he needs to improve on.

So, to improve on this Smith needs 56 runs.

> Find the difference between Smith and Phillips. Smith needs 1 more.

Now try these

1 Hatton's netball team scored the following goals in 8 matches.

41	33	35	38	36	36	35	38

Georgie's team scored the following goals in 6 matches.

47	29	52	31	38	28

Ann claims Hatton's team did the best. Is she correct?
Explain your answer.

2 Three meals have a mean average price of £8.97.
All of the meals have a different price.
Write down the possible price of each meal.

3 Write down two sets of numbers with the same mean but
a a different median
b a different mode
c a different range.

4 A hospital outpatients department has promised that waiting times will be on average 1 hour.
The waiting times (in minutes) of the first 9 patients are given below.

54	75	49	45	72	63	29	78	85

What is the maximum time the next patient can be kept waiting if they are to meet their target?

5 The weights (g) of 10 lambs were recorded by Farmer Pearce.

1000	1250	2000	1875	1400	1650	1325	1125	1450	1700

Farmer Hicken also has 10 lambs.
The range of weights for Farmer Hicken's lambs was 2.5 kg.
The mean weight of Farmer Hicken's lambs was 1.5 kg.
Test the hypothesis that Farmer Hicken's lambs were bigger than Farmer Pearce's lambs.

6

5 day forecast- Florida

	Monday	Tuesday	Wednesday	Thursday	Friday
High	27°C	27°C	27°C	27°C	27°C
Low	13°C	14°C	16°C	16°C	16°C
Humidity	0%	1%	5%	10%	20%

5 day forecast- Cuba, Varadero

	Monday	Tuesday	Wednesday	Thursday	Friday
High	25°C	26°C	26°C	27°C	30°C
Low	19°C	21°C	21°C	21°C	17°C
Humidity	0%	10%	20%	20%	20%

5 day forecast- Egypt, Red Sea

	Monday	Tuesday	Wednesday	Thursday	Friday
High	27°C	25°C	25°C	26°C	27°C
Low	17°C	16°C	14°C	16°C	17°C
Humidity	0%	0%	0%	0%	0%

Sonja and John are planning their honeymoon for after their wedding in November.
They are trying to decide where to go.
The weather for a week in November at three different resorts is shown in the charts above.
Recommend one of these resorts, giving evidence to show it has the best weather.

PROBABILITY

The following question tests both your ability to select and apply a method in the context of choosing the best strategy to win a game (AO2) and your ability to analyse and interpret problems (AO3). The AO2 skills come into the first part. Showing the outcome space in a table is the most efficient way to compare the probabilities but some students may just produce a list of possible outcomes. Your AO3 skills are needed in both parts of this question as you will need to give a reasoned explanation for your answer.

Example

In a game the player has a choice of throwing 1 or 2 dice.
The winning score is 6.
Joshua says 'You are more likely to win if you throw 2 dice'.

a Is Joshua correct? Explain your answer.
b Is it possible to have a winning score which is equally likely whether 1 or 2 dice is thrown? Explain your answer.

Solution

a 1 dice: numbers thrown are 1, 2, 3, 4, 5, 6;
   probability of a 6 is $\frac{1}{6}$.
   2 dice: the outcome space is

	1	2	3	4	5	6
1	2	3	4	5	6	7
2	3	4	5	6	7	8
3	4	5	6	7	8	9
4	5	6	7	8	9	10
5	6	7	8	9	10	11
6	7	8	9	10	11	12

> Work out the probability by writing down the outcome space.

> The outcome space is useful in explaining your answer.

The probability of a total of 6 with two dice is $\frac{5}{36}$.
So, Joshua is incorrect. Throwing 1 dice is more likely to win the game.

b The likelihood of any number 1 to 6 being thrown on a single dice is $\frac{1}{6}$.
   The likelihood of a number greater than 6 being thrown on a single dice is 0.
   The only number with a probability of $\frac{1}{6}$ when 2 dice are thrown is 7, which is not possible on a single dice.
   It is impossible to choose a winning score which is equally likely whether 1 or 2 dice are thrown.

1 A class did a survey of how they travelled to school.
The results are shown in the table below.

	Number of People
Car	9
Bus	7
Walk	10
Cycle	4

Explain why the probability of a student selected at random travelling to school by bus is not $\frac{1}{4}$.

2 Ahmed says 'I like multiple choice tests because I can get half the marks by guessing'.
a Is he correct?
b Explain your answer.

3 Three coins are tossed together.
What is the probability that they all come down the same – all heads or all tails?
Explain your answer.

4 The advert shows a special offer for lunch in a restaurant.
If the customer chooses at random, what is the probability
of them choosing soup, a pie and fruit?

Meal Deal

Starter   Soup
Orange Juice

Main   Meat Pie
Fish Pie
Veggie Burger

Sweet   Ice Cream
Fruit
Cheese

5 In a game of chance a shape is chosen at random.
The table shows the shapes and the probability that they will be chosen.

☺	✈	📖	🔔
0.2	0.4		0.1

Work out the probability that the book will be chosen.

6 A travel agent collected information from 100 people about when they took their holidays.
He found that 26 went in September, 42 preferred an August holiday and the rest went in July.
A total of 57 took their holiday in a hotel, 16 of these in September. 19 people took a self-catering holiday in August.
Work out the probability of a person selected at random taking a holiday in a hotel in August.

F
A03

A03

E
A02
A03

A02
A03

D

C
A02
A03

A balanced diet is central to overall good health. To help consumers make healthy choices nutritional information is printed on most food items.

1. Samantha invites her friends round for dinner. Together they eat a bag of chicken nuggets and a pizza, which they cut into eight slices.

   Samantha has 4 slices of pizza with 5 chicken nuggets. Daisy has 3 slices of pizza with 10 nuggets and Darren has the rest of the pizza with 12 nuggets.

   The tables show some nutritional information about the pizza and the chicken nuggets.

Pizza

Typical values	Per 100g	Per slice
Energy	1000kJ	494kJ
Protein	9.3g	4.6g
Carbohydrates	28.7g	14.2g
Fat	9.6g	4.8g
Fibre	2.3g	1.1g
Salt	1.0g	0.5g

Chicken Nuggets

Typical values	Per 100g	Per nugget
Energy	1150kJ	189kJ
Protein	9.7g	1.6g
Carbohydrates	18.2g	3.0g
Fat	18.2g	3.0g
Fibre	1.7g	0.3g
Salt	1.0g	0.2g

QUESTION

Compare the amount of fat and salt eaten by each of the three friends.

LINKS

- For **Question 1** you need to be able to read data from tables. You learnt how to do this in **Chapter 1**.

- You need to understand dual bar charts for **Question 2**. You learnt about them in **Chapter 2**.

- You learnt about interpreting pie charts in **Chapter 2**. You will use this in **Question 3**.

Healthy Choice Fitness Gym

2. In 2007–08 there were approximately 600 000 children in Reception classes and 650 000 in Year 6.

The National Child Measurement Program details on weight are shown in the dual bar chart.

QUESTION

Compare the numbers of obese and overweight children in Reception and Year 6.

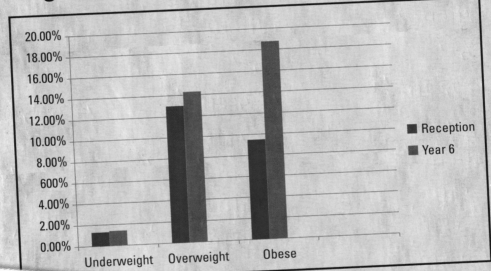

The National Child Measurement Program details on weight 2007–08

Rochelle's Exercise type

- Flexibility
- Aerobic
- Anaerobic

3. Rochelle joins the gym to improve her fitness. Her instructor gives her a pie chart showing the proportion of time she should spend on three types of exercise.

QUESTION

When Rochelle goes to the gym and spends 2 hours exercising, approximately how long should she spend on each type of exercise?

FS

To pass your driving test you need to know stopping distances for different speeds.

Learning to drive a car can be expensive so it is a good idea to write a budget before starting lessons.

1. When revising for the theory part of the driving test, information from a table is easier to remember than from a composite bar chart.

2. Use the information below to estimate the cost of passing the driving test. You need a theory test guide and a minimum of 30 hours of lessons. You also need to pass the theory test and the practical test.

QUESTION

QUESTION

Draw and complete a suitable table (for the different speeds) from the composite bar chart.

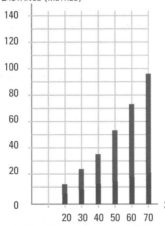

DISTANCE (METRES)

■ Breaking distance   ■ Thinking distance

Learner Test Information

Theory test fees	Price
Standard fee for car and motorcycle	£31
Multiple choice questions for bus and lorry drivers	£35
Hazard perception for bus and lorry drivers	£15
Driver CPC theory test case studies for bus and lorry drivers	£30
Potential approved driving instructor	£90

Practical test type	Weekday price/ Evening and weekend price
Car	£62 / £75
Tractor and other specialist vehicle	£62 / £75
Motorcycle; module 1	£15.50 / £15.50
Motorcycle; module 2	£15.50 / £15.50
Lorry and bus	£115 / £141
Driver CPC	£55 / £63
Car and trailer	£115 / £141

LINKS

- For **Question 1** you need to be able to interpret composite bar charts. You learnt how to do this in **Chapter 2**.

- You learnt how to round in **Chapter 1**. You will need to do this in **Question 2**.

- You need to be able to read two-way tables in **Question 3**. You learnt this in **Chapter 1**.

When buying a second-hand car there are lots of factors to consider. A used car guide can help you estimate the price and avoid paying too much.

3. Josh sees an 0352 reg car with a milage of 87 000 miles on the clock for sale privately. To get some idea of what price he might have to pay he consults a guide. There are two tables. Table 1 shows the price according to age and a set mileage, and Table 2 shows an adjustment for mileage above the set mileage.

These prices are adjusted when the mileage differs from the stated value by more than 1000 miles. The amount depends on the dealer price, the code and how many thousands of miles more or less there are on the clock.

Example: If the Dealer price is £4000 and the Code is D, then for each 1000 miles over the stated value the price has to be reduced by £130.

Work out an estimated price for the car that Josh has seen for sale.

QUESTION

Table 1

Table 2

AUTO TRADE **GUIDE**

For sale

Reg	New (£)	Dealer (£)	Private (£)	Trade (£)	Mileage	Code
0202	9400	2105	1875	1840	80 000	B
0252	9795	2205	1900	1845	80 000	B
0352	9895	2355	2090	2050	70 000	B
0303	9995	2470	2175	2135	70 000	B
0353	9995	2595	2435	2475	60 000	B

Dealer price	Code				
	A	B	C	D	E
Up to £999	0	0	10	20	30
£1000–£1999	0	5	35	50	55
£2000–£3999	5	10	60	80	120
£4000–£6999	10	25	95	130	210
£6999–£10 999	30	50	120	180	390
£11 000+	50	60	160	200	420

Answers

F1 Answers

1.1 Get ready

a Survey of classmates
b e.g. internet
c e.g. internet

Exercise 1A

1 15 metres
2 0.85 metre
3 250
4 Specify the problem.
  Decide what information to collect.
  Collect the information.
  Present and display the information.
  Interpret the findings.
  Act on the conclusions drawn from the findings.
5 **a** Type of house
  b Garden size
  c Number of bedrooms, Price
6 **a** Number of hours boys spend watching television
    Number of hours girls spend watching television
  b Continuous data

1.2 Get ready

a 3   **b** 6   **c** 10

Exercise 1B

1 **a**

Colour	Tally	Frequency
Silver	ЖЖ Ж I	11
White	I	1
Blue	Ж	5
Black	IIII	4
Red	Ж IIII	9
Total		30

  b Silver

2 **a**

Age (years)	Tally	Frequency
13	IIII	4
14	Ж II	7
15	Ж IIII	9
16	Ж Ж	10
Total		30

  b 11 members
3 **a** 138 cm   **b** 1.38 m

4 **a** Train A
  b The last train arrives at 17:30, which is 5.30 pm.
5 **a**

Length (cm)	Tally	Frequency
5–6	Ж I	6
7–8	Ж I	6
9–10	Ж III	8
11–12	IIII	4
Total		24

  b 6 worms
6 No. She needs 110 g $\times$ 10 = 1100 g = 1.1 kg
7 **a** 20 glasses   **b** 3 bottles   **c** £3.60

1.3 Get ready

Tally chart

Exercise 1C

1 It does not allow for more than 4 times. The boxes overlap.
2 It does not give categories for the answer. Some people might not want to give their precise age.
3 It does not allow for 'No'.
  The question is biased, as it starts 'Do you agree …'.

1.4 Get ready

Depends on class size.
For a class of 30 students it takes 450 seconds or 7.5 minutes.

Exercise 1D

1 The sample is too small.
  It may not include people who shop on other days.
  It may not include people who play sport on Saturday mornings.
2 The sample only includes students from one year.
3 The sample is small.
  The people may not read the magazine.

1.5 Get ready

A 12
B 6

Exercise 1E

1

	Music	Drama	Total
Art	7	6	13
PE	5	12	17
Total	12	18	30

2

	Large	Small	Total
Vanilla	8	10	18
Chocolate	6	4	10
Total	14	14	28

3 a

	Junior	Senior	Family	Total
Full week	14	36	24	74
Weekends	28	56	20	104
Total	42	92	44	178

b 28 weekend junior members

4 a

	Pizza	Salad	Pasta	Total
Gateau	12	10	3	25
Ice cream	10	10	20	40
Fruit	4	2	1	7
Total	26	22	24	72

b 20 people
c 72 people

Exercise 1F

1 a 50.7 mm   **b** 1.2°C   **c** October
2 a 63 moons   **b** −200°C   **c** Mercury
   d Venus   **e** 4 planets
3 a 90 minutes   **b** Newcastle
   c London to Birmingham   **d** London to Inverness
4 5 km, 1 km, 5 km, 9 km, 14 km
5 1.6 cm, 0.9 cm, 2.5 cm, 1.6 cm, 3.5 cm
6 a £1070
   b They could have travelled in January, or stayed for less time.

Review exercise

1 a

Country	Tally	Frequency
Australia			1
France	||||	4
Italy	|||||	5
Spain	|||	3
USA	||||| ||	7

b 20

2 a

Length (cm)	Tally	Frequency
13					3
14								6
15						4
16					3
17				2

b 3

3 a There is no set period of time.
     There is no option for 0 texts.
   b They may not be representative of the whole population.
4 a 10 centime
   b 1 dollar
5 a Volvo
   b Mazda
6 **i** The colours of walls in each classroom
  ii Number of school meals sold;
     the cost of a school outing
 iii Heights of students

7 a

+	1	2	3	4	5	6
1	2	3	4	5	6	7
2	3	4	5	6	7	8
3	4	5	6	7	8	9
4	5	6	7	8	9	10

b (1, 4), (2, 3), (3, 2), (4, 1)
c (4, 4), (5, 3), (6, 2)

8 The question doesn't specify a length of time and the options for the response boxes overlap. The sample is biased as her class may not be representative of the whole population.

9 The question doesn't specify a length of time. It is not clear what the options for the response boxes represent.
Students' questions, for example:
How many times do you visit the cinema each month?
☐ Never   ☐ 1 or 2   ☐ 3 or 4   ☐ 5 or more

10 How many times do you shop at the supermarket each month?
☐ Never   ☐ 1 or 2   ☐ 3 or 4   ☐ 5 or more

11 How many emails do you send per week?
☐ None   ☐ 1 to 3   ☐ 4 to 6   ☐ 7 or more

12 People leaving the cinema are more likely to be frequent cinema goers than the population in general.
She should also question men.

13

Preferred animal	Tally	Frequency
Lion		
Tiger		
Elephant		
Monkey		
Giraffe		

14

Country	Tally	Frequency
France		5
Spain		7
Italy		4
England		4

15 a £2510
   b £1500
16 497 miles

Answers

17 a

	Small	Medium	Large	Total
Pine	7	12	4	23
Oak	10	16	8	34
Yew	3	8	2	13
Total	20	36	14	70

18

	Time
Kai leaves home	10:06
Train departs Manchester	10:16
Train arrives Preston	11:00
Kai arrives for interview	11:20
Interview finishes	12:30
Train leaves Preston	15:45
Train arrives Manchester	16:27
Kai arrives home	16:37

19 a Other classes may be voting differently.
b 80 votes
20 a 1400
b The 6 acres field may not be representative of the whole farm.

F2 Answers

2.1 Get ready

1 Discrete quantitative
2 Qualitative data
3 Continuous quantitative data

Exercise 2A

1 a Thursday **b** 100 emails **c** 80 emails **d** 70 emails
2 a Juice **b** 60 drinks **c** 35 drinks **d** 210 drinks
3 a

Margherita	⊕ ⊕ ◹
BBQ Chicken	⊕ ⊕ ⊕ ⊕
Hawaiian	⊕ ⊕ ◔
Meat feast	⊕ ⊕ ◖

b Margherita: 18 pizzas; BBQ chicken 32 pizzas; Hawaiian 22 pizzas; Meat feast 20 pizzas

4

English	🏃 🏃 🏃
Mathematics	🏃 🏃 🏃 🏃
Spanish	🏃 🏃
Science	🏃 🏃 🏃 🏃 🏃
Technology	🏃 🏃

Key
🏃 represents two students

5

Walk	⊞ ⊞
Bus	⊞ ⊞ ⊞ ⊞ ⊞ ⊞ ⊞ ⊞ ⊞ ⊞
Train	⊞
Cycle	⊞ ⊞ ⊞ ⊞
Car	⊞

Key
⊞ represents four students

2.2 Get ready

1 270°
2 $\frac{1}{20}$
3 70°

Exercise 2B

1 50°
2 a 90°
b 4 hours
3 a

City	Reading	Swindon	Bristol	Cardiff
Angle	$\frac{6}{40} \times 360$ $= 54°$	$\frac{5}{40} \times 360$ $= 45°$	$\frac{9}{40} \times 360$ $= 81°$	$\frac{20}{40} \times 360$ $= 180°$

b

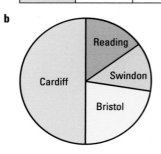

4 a

Fruit	Strawberry	Apple	Banana	Grape	Orange
Angle	$\frac{25}{60} \times 360 =$ $150°$	$\frac{15}{60} \times 360$ $= 90°$	$\frac{6}{60} \times 60$ $= 36°$	$\frac{9}{60} \times 360$ $= 54°$	$\frac{5}{60} \times 360$ $= 30°$

b

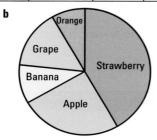

5

Time in minutes	Angle
Less than 10	$\frac{3}{30} \times 360 = 36°$
Between 10 and <15	$\frac{4}{30} \times 360 = 48°$
Between 15 and 30	$\frac{17}{30} \times 360 = 144°$
More than 30	$\frac{11}{30} \times 360 = 132°$

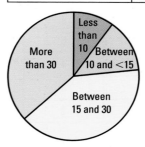

6

Category	Thriller	Classic	Romance	Non-fiction
Angle	$\frac{120}{540} \times 360$ $= 80°$	$\frac{60}{540} \times 360$ $= 40°$	$\frac{270}{540} \times 360$ $= 180°$	$\frac{90}{540} \times 360$ $= 60°$

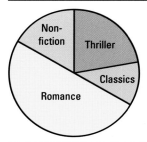

7

Type of car	Ford	Nissan	Toyota	Renault
Angle	$\frac{24}{90} \times 360$ $= 96°$	$\frac{30}{90} \times 360$ $= 120°$	$\frac{27}{90} \times 360$ $= 108°$	$\frac{9}{90} \times 360$ $= 36°$

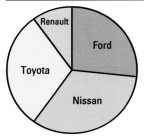

8

Day	Monday	Tuesday	Wednesday	Thursday	Friday
Angle	$\frac{7}{36} \times 360$ $= 70°$	$\frac{8}{36} \times 360$ $= 80°$	$\frac{10}{36} \times 360$ $= 100°$	$\frac{6}{36} \times 360°$ $= 60°$	$\frac{5}{36} \times 360$ $= 50°$

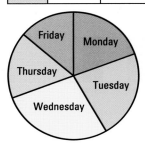

Exercise 2C

1. a Going out with friends   b Reading
   c $\frac{1}{3}$ d 40 adults
2. a Spain   b 4°   c 20 girls
   d 108°   e 27 girls
3.

Activity	Angle	Number of hours
Sleep	120°	8
School	105°	7
Play	30°	2
Watch TV	60°	4
Eat	15°	1
Homework	30°	2

4. a $\frac{1}{4}$ b 300 people
   c $3\frac{1}{3}$ people   d 160 people
5. a 2°   b 180 people
   c Vanilla and chocolate. They have the largest angles.
6. a $\frac{1}{5}$ b 60 students

2.3 Get ready

1. 25
2. 84
3. 720
4. 140

Exercise 2D

1. 68 mm
2. a 7 students   b 26 students
3. a 5 cars   b Garage F   c 33 cars
4. a Sam   b 3 hours   c Caitlin and Laura
   d Owen
5.

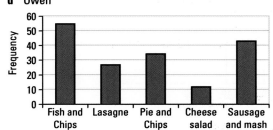

2.4 Get ready

1. a Red   b Blue

Exercise 2E

1. a 30°C   b 33°C   c Resort G
   d Resorts C and F   e Resort A
2. a Factory A   b 45 males   c 45 people
   d 130 people   e Factory A. It has more workers.
3. a Shortbread   b Protein   c 25%
4.

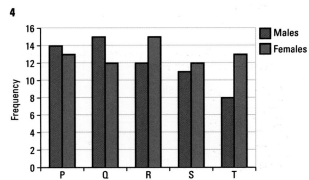

2.5 Get ready

1. a C   b E   c A and D

Exercise 2F

1. a 4 times   b Number 6   c 41 times
2. a 10 cars   b 2 people   c 100 cars   d 110 people

Answers

3 a Because it represents continuous data.
b 5 runners **c** 6 runners **d** 20 runners

4

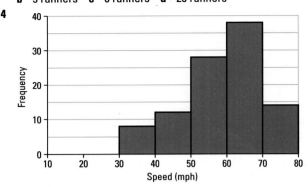

2.6 Get ready

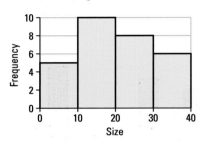

Exercise 2G

1 a, b

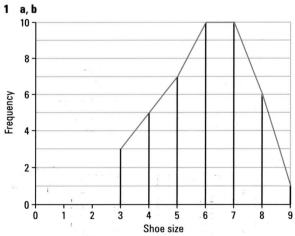

2 a, b

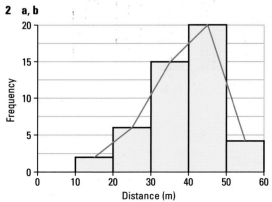

3 a Once **b** 4 times **c** $\frac{1}{4}$
d The train, because the blue line is above the red line for the higher time values.

Review exercise

1 a i 8 **ii** 10
b

2 a 7 TVs **b** Monday
c Tuesday and Wednesday
3 a 3 students **b** Cat **c** 22 students
4 a 20 plates
b 15
c

Monday	○ ○
Tuesday	○ ◖
Wednesday	○ ○ ○
Thursday	○
Friday	○ ○ ○ ○
Saturday	○ ○ ◖

5 a

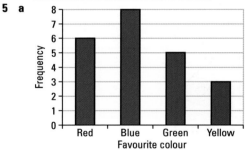

b Blue
6 a Wednesday and Friday
b 320 minutes or 5 hours 20 minutes
7 a 14 boys
b 5 girls
c

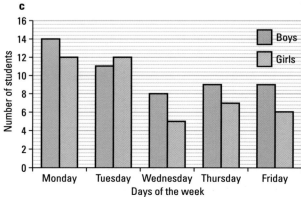

d Tuesday

8 a $\frac{1}{4}$

b 60 students

9

Subject	Number of students	Angle
Art	12	72°
French	10	60°
History	20	120°
Music	18	108°

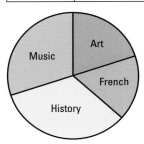

10

Drink	Frequency	Angle
Hot chocolate	20	80°
Soup	15	60°
Coffee	25	100°
Tea	30	120°

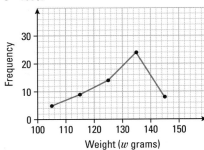

11 a 9 am

b Jose's temperature steadily reduced.

12 a 18%

b 5%

c 100%

13

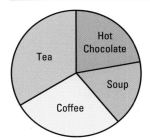

14 a $\frac{5}{18}$

b **i** 16 students

ii 72 students

c The pie chart doesn't give frequencies, only proportions.

15

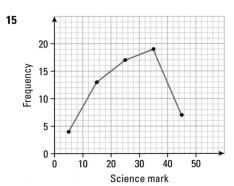

16

Protein	Carbohydrate	Fibre	Other
6 g	16 g	5 g	93 g
$\frac{6}{120} \times 360$ $= 18°$	$\frac{16}{120} \times 360$ $= 48°$	$\frac{5}{120} \times 360$ $= 15°$	$\frac{93}{120} \times 360$ $= 279°$

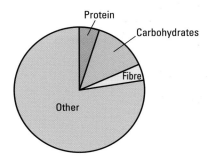

17 Students' composite bar charts

F3 Answers

3.1 Get ready

a 72 **b** 65

Exercise 3A

1 a £5.50 **b** 670 coins **c** 67 coins

2 2.05 metres

3 144 questionnaires

4 £3.92

5 a 36 **b** 27 **c** 7

d 4 **e** 3

6 £389.96

3.2 Get ready

1 a 284 296 302 325 336

b 0.55 0.59 0.6 0.61 0.625

2 a 38 times **b** Yellow **c** Two more times

Exercise 3B

1 a 2 **b** 10 and 12 **c** No mode **d** Dog

2 16

3 Silver

4 £7.20 and £8.20

Exercise 3C

1 a 5   b 7   c 6.5   d 4   e 5.5
2 1.2°C
3 39.5 thousands of tonnes
4 £26 100

Exercise 3D

1 a 6   b 5   c 7.5
2 4 meals
3 a 190 cm   b 186 cm   c 185 cm
4 a No mode   b 131 emails   c 131.5 emails

3.3 Get ready

1 5
2 5a

Exercise 3E

1 4x
2 4x + 20y pence
3 a Expression   b Equation   c Formula
4 nr pence
5 70 fish
6 a 3x + 4.5 pounds
   b 3y + 3 = 3x + 4.5

3.4 Get ready

a 8   b 6   c 6

Exercise 3F

1 The value of the mean will be affected by the extreme value of the most expensive jumper.
2 a The mode
   b No. The mode is the lowest of the prices of cars.
3 a 2 emails   b 6 emails   c 6 emails
   d The value of the mode is low compared to the number of junk emails received on many days. The value of the mean is affected by the extreme value of 17. The median is the best average to represent these data.
4 Mode = 10 and 13 minutes
   Median = 13 minutes
   Mean = $\dfrac{10 + 10 + 13 + 13 + 16 + 17 + 40}{7}$ = 17 minutes
   The data is numeric and there is one extreme value, so the median is the best average to use.

3.5 Get ready

a 13, 2
b 29, 19
c 161, 130

Exercise 3G

1 a 19   b 11   c 6
2 No. Petra has used the first and last scores, which are not the lowest and highest ones.
   Range = 25 − 11 = 14

3 a Economics: range = 44; Psychology: range = 15
   b Psychology has the most consistent marks, because the range is smaller.
4 a Machine 1: range = 3 ml; Machine 2: range = 6 ml
   b Machine 1: mean = 30 ml; Machine 2: mean = 30 ml
   c Both machines filled the bottles with the same mean amount of water. Machine 1 had a smaller range. The amounts of water were less spread out which shows that the machine was more consistent.
5 Max Rangers:
   Mean =
   $$\dfrac{170 + 172 + 180 + 190 + 184 + 179 + 176 + 183 + 186 + 190 + 170}{11}$$
   = 180 cm
   Range = 190 − 170 = 20

   Red United:
   Mean =
   $$\dfrac{179 + 190 + 187 + 170 + 180 + 182 + 163 + 188 + 181 + 190 + 179}{11}$$
   = 180.818181... = 180.8 cm (to 1 d.p.)
   Range = 190 − 163 = 27
   The mean heights are very close but Red United had a wider spread due to an extreme value (163).

3.6 Get ready

1 26 35 42 58
2 151 152 153 154
3 0.1 0.2 0.4 0.5
4 0.1 0.11 0.12 0.9

Exercise 3H

1

0	1	2	3	4	6		
1	2	2	2	4	6		
2	2	3	4	5	7	9	
3	0	2	3	4	5	6	8
4	2	3	6	7			

2

0	6	8	9	9				
1	0	2	4	5	7	7	7	8
2	1	2	2	5	6	7		
3	1	9						

3 a 21 weeks   b 26 cars
   c 26 cars   d 31 cars

4

0	2	2	3	3	5	5	7	8	
1	0	2	4	5	6	6	6	8	8
2	0	2	3	3	3	4			
3	0								

   b 16 and 23 minutes   c 15.5 minutes
   d 28 minutes

3.7 Get ready

1 a 5 **b** 30

Exercise 3I

1 a 1 car **b** 2 cars **c** 2 cars
2 a 65 g **b** 65 g **c** 65.2 g
3 a 7 peas **b** 7 peas **c** 6.5 peas

3.8 Get ready

1 a Discrete **c** Discrete **c** Continuous
2 a False **c** True **c** False

Exercise 3J

1 a 6 to 8 **b** 6 to 8
2 a 11 to 15 **b** 11 to 15
3 a $1.1 \leqslant d < 1.3$ **b** $1.3 \leqslant d < 1.5$

3.9 Get ready

a 7 **b** 60 **c** 75.5
d 0.8 **e** 125 000

Exercise 3K

1 7.4 packets
2 1.5 breakdowns
3 11.125 minutes

3.10 Get ready

a 81 **b** 6

Exercise 3L

1 a 12.96 **b** 91.125 **c** 42.5 **d** 32
2 1.73 m
3 a 302
 b About 300 books
4 a 6 or 7 **b** 6.9

Review exercise

1 a 7 **b** 6
 c 6 **d** 3
2 a £290 **b** £305
 c £342 **d** £160
3 a £379 **b** £400
 c £150 **d** £65
4 a 6 **b** 6.2
5 30 mm
6 a 3.5 **b** 3.6 **c** 4
7 a 65 kg **b** 34 kg
8 a 15 biscuits
 b 25 oat crunchies
9 1, 4, 5, 5, 5; 2, 3, 5, 5, 5; 1, 3, 5, 5, 6; 2, 2, 5, 5, 6; 1, 2, 5, 5, 7; 1, 1, 5, 5, 8

10 a 29 **b** 46 **c** 46 **d** 45
11 a £22 **b** £34 **c** £46.70
 d The median is the best average here. The mode is the lowest value and the mean is distorted by the expensive dress (£180).
12 a Eating apple: mean 138.9 g, range 18 g
 Cooking apple: mean 148 g, range 26 g
 b On average the cooking apples are heavier, but they vary in weight more than the eating apples.
13 a

4	6 8
5	1 2 8
6	0 3 4 6 8
7	4 7 8 9
8	7

 4|5 stands for 45 kg
 b 5 people
 c 41 kg
14 1.9 cups of coffee
15

2	3 7
3	1 4 5 6 8
4	1 2 4 5 5
5	0 2 3

 4|5 stands for 45 kg
16 As some (injured!) spiders will have less than eight legs, the mean number of legs will be less than eight. So the statement can be true.
17 a The mode is 7.
 b 6.3 rooms, to 1 d.p.
18 The mean for males is 48 and the range is 48.
 The mean for females is 61.1 and the range is 70.
 On average the females get higher scores, but their scores vary more.
19 a Expression
 b 84
 c This is a suitable number as there are already two spare bottles per class.
20 Meena must score $70 \times 6 = 420$ marks in total on the 6 tests to get an average score of 70.
 So far she has $64 \times 5 = 320$ marks.
 Therefore she needs $420 - 320 = 100$ marks on the sixth test.
21 If you want to show that the average is high use the mean (£30 000). If you want to show that the average is low use the mode or the median (both £10 000).
22 a 10 to 12 and 13 to 15 are both modal classes.
 b 13 to 15
 c £13.50
23 a $31 \leqslant h < 33$
 b $29 \leqslant h < 31$
 c 30.36 cm
24 19 minutes
25 18.4 minutes
26 a $10\,000 < x \leqslant 14\,000$
 b $14\,000 < x \leqslant 16\,000$

F4 Answers

Exercise 4A

1 a £7 **b** 5.5 euros

2 a 94 cm² **b** 3.9 cm

3 a

x	0	1	2	3	4	5
$y = 2x$	0	2	4	6	8	10

b

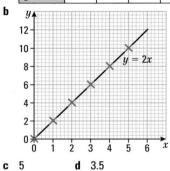

c 5 **d** 3.5

4.2 Get ready

1 a $y = 3$ **b** $y = 5$ **c** $y = 8$

2

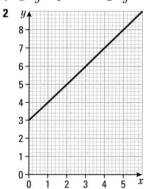

Exercise 4B

1 a–c

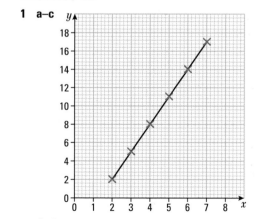

d 3

2 1.5

3 2

4.3 Get ready

1 (0, 1) and (4, 4)

2

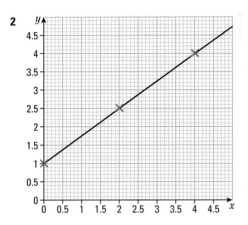

Exercise 4C

1 a £12.80

b 21 minutes

2 a **i** 68°F **ii** 212°F **iii** 97°F

b **i** 60°C **ii** 16°C **iii** 31°C

3 a

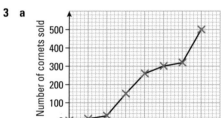

b 7th hour

4.4 Get ready

1 A = 3.8

2 B = 60.25

3 C = 44.75
D = 45.5

Exercise 4D

1 The higher the number of breaths per minute the higher the pulse rate.

2 a

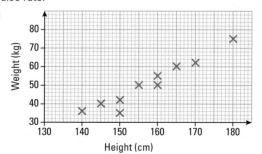

b The greater the height the larger the weight.

3 a

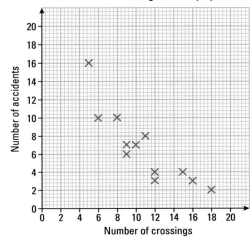

b The heavier the car the higher its top speed.

4

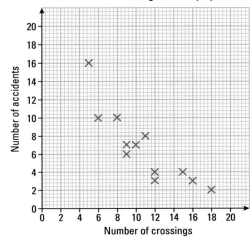

The more crossings there are the fewer the number of accidents.

4.5 Get ready

August, September, October, November, December

Exercise 4E

1 No correlation

2 a Negative correlation
b As the age of the car increases the cost decreases.

3

Variables	Positive correlation	Negative correlation	No correlation
Height and Weight of people	✓		
Intelligence and Weight of people			✓
Size of garden and Number of birds	✓		
Age and Running speed of adults		✓	
Height and Shoe size of people	✓		
Age of cars and Engine size			✓
Arm length and Leg length of people	✓		

4 a

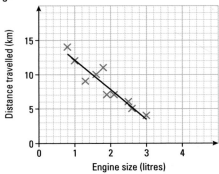

b There is positive correlation: the higher the temperature the more bottles of water Jacob sells.

4.6 Get ready

About £6000

Exercise 4F

1 a Negative correlation
b, c

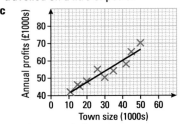

d The larger the engine size the lower the distance travelled on a litre of petrol.

2 a, c

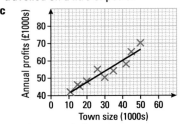

b Positive correlation
d The greater the town size the bigger the profits.

3 a, c

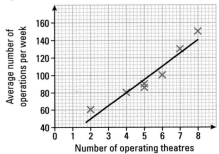

b Positive correlation
d The higher the number of operating theatres the higher the average number of operations per week.

Answers

4.5 Get ready

(5, 4.7)

Exercise 4G

1 **a** Positive correlation
  b **i** £70 000   **ii** 25 000 models
2 **a** Negative correlation
  b **i** 30 units   **ii** 4.8°C
3 **a** 147
  b 52 years
  c Positive correlation: the older a man is the higher his blood pressure.

Review exercise

1 **a** Positive correlation
  b

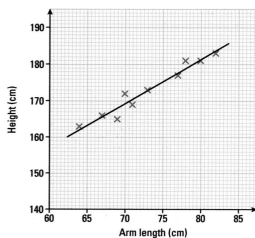

  c 175 cm

2 **a** Negative correlation
  b

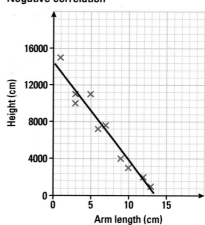

3 **a, c**

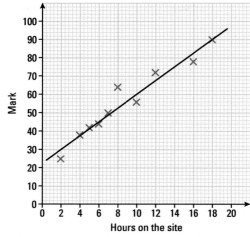

  b Positive correlation
4 **a** About −1
  b 9.4 minutes
  c Negative correlation
  b The older the apprentices the quicker they learn skills
5 **a, b**

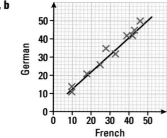

  c About 1
  d Students A, B, C and D got less than 26 in at least one exam. $\frac{4}{10} = \frac{2}{5}$ students
6 **a, c**

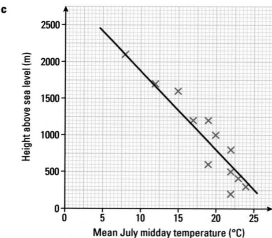

  b Negative correlation
  c 11°C
  d 1000 m

7 a Negative correlation: the older the car the lower its value.

b

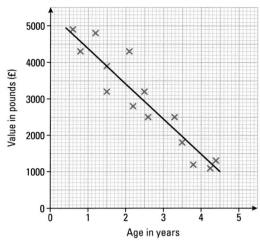

c £2450   **d** 1.9 years

8 a Positive correlation: the greater the weight the taller the height.

b

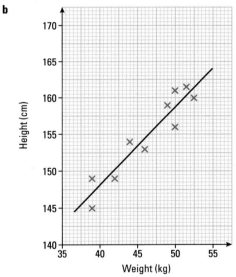

c 155.5 cm

9 a Negative correlation

b

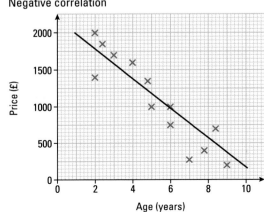

c 3.4 years

10 a Approximately £9000

b The one-year-old Mini is more expensive than expected. It may have extra features or a very low milage.

F5 Answers

5.1 Get ready

Certain
Impossible

Exercise 5A

1 Probability scales showing:
  a certain   **b** impossible   **c** even chance
  d likely   **e** unlikely
2 Students' examples
3 Probability scale showing 'unlikely'
4 Students' opinions
5 a 0.5, 0.8, 0.25, 0.36
  b $\frac{3}{10}, \frac{1}{4}, \frac{7}{20}, \frac{31}{50}$
  c 55%, 67%, 10%, 60%
6 $\frac{1}{10}$, 0.2, 48%, $\frac{4}{5}$

5.2 Get ready

Fraction	$\frac{3}{10}$	$\frac{6}{10}$	$\frac{3}{8}$	$\frac{13}{20}$
Decimal	0.3	0.6	0.375	0.65
Percentage	30%	60%	37.5%	65%

Exercise 5B

1 a $\frac{3}{8}$ **b** $\frac{3}{8}$ **c** $\frac{6}{8} = \frac{3}{4}$
2 a $\frac{3}{8}$ **b** $\frac{2}{8} = \frac{1}{4}$ **c** $\frac{2}{8} = \frac{1}{4}$ **d** $\frac{1}{8}$
3 a $\frac{3}{10}$ **b** $\frac{7}{10}$ **c** 0
4 a $\frac{1}{10}$ **b** $\frac{3}{10}$ **c** $\frac{2}{10} = \frac{1}{5}$
  d $\frac{6}{10} = \frac{3}{5}$ **e** 0
5 a $\frac{1}{6}$ **b** $\frac{2}{6} = \frac{1}{3}$ **c** $\frac{3}{6} = \frac{1}{2}$ **d** $\frac{4}{6} = \frac{2}{3}$
  e 0   **f** $\frac{3}{6} = \frac{1}{2}$
6 a $\frac{67}{120}$ **b** $\frac{53}{120}$
7 a $\frac{3}{15} = \frac{1}{5}$ **b** $\frac{7}{15}$ **c** $\frac{5}{15} = \frac{1}{3}$ **d** $\frac{10}{15} = \frac{2}{3}$
  e $\frac{8}{15}$ **f** $\frac{1}{5}$

5.3 Get ready

a 0.3   **b** 0.4   **c** $\frac{1}{2}$ **d** $\frac{1}{4}$

Exercise 5C

1 0.7
2 0.85
3 $\frac{1}{3}$
4 $\frac{50}{53}$
5 0.3
6 0.36
7 0.675
8 P(train is not late) = 1 − 0.32 = 0.68

Answers

Exercise 5D

1 0.3
2 0.1
3 a 0.17 **b** 0.81 **c** 0.64
4 0.25
5 $\frac{1}{3}$
6 $\frac{1}{10}$

5.4 Get ready

1 a $\frac{1}{4}$ **b** $\frac{3}{5}$
2 a $\frac{3}{4}$ **b** $\frac{7}{20}$

Exercise 5E

1 85%
2 £240
3 £112.50
4 £1416
5 $\frac{7}{10} \times 100 = 70\%$. So Jack has worked out the cost of the CD after a 30% discount.
$\frac{20}{100} \times 10 = £2$
$10 - 2 = £8$
$\frac{10}{100} \times 8 = 0.8$
$8 - 0.8 = £7.20$
Jack has taken off 30% in one go, but the shopkeeper has taken off 20% and then 10% from the discounted price.

5.5 Get ready

a heads or tails **b** 1, 2, 3, 4, 5 or 6 **c** win, lose or draw

Exercise 5F

1

Dice		
6	(H, 6)	(T, 6)
5	(H, 5)	(T, 5)
4	(H, 4)	(T, 4)
3	(H, 3)	(T, 3)
2	(H, 2)	(T, 2)
1	(H, 1)	(T, 1)
	H	T
	Coin	

2 a $\frac{1}{8}$ **b** $\frac{1}{6}$ **c** $\frac{5}{12}$
3 a $\frac{1}{16}$ **b** $\frac{4}{16} = \frac{1}{4}$
c $\frac{6}{16} = \frac{3}{8}$ **d** $\frac{7}{16}$
e 1 **f** $\frac{9}{16}$ **g** 0

4

Spinner 1			
3	(1, 3)	(2, 3)	(3, 3)
2	(1, 2)	(2, 2)	(3, 2)
1	(1, 1)	(2, 1)	(3, 1)
	1	2	3
		Spinner 2	

5 a

Sheet			
W	(W, W)	(G, W)	(O, W)
Y	(W, Y)	(G, Y)	(O, Y)
B	(W, B)	(G, B)	(O, B)
G	(W, G)	(G, G)	(O, G)
	W	G	O
		Pillow case	

b i $\frac{2}{12} = \frac{1}{6}$ **ii** $\frac{5}{6}$

6 $P(2) = \frac{1}{2}$, $P(3) = \frac{2}{12}$, $P(4) = \frac{3}{12}$, $P(5) = \frac{3}{12}$, $P(6) = \frac{2}{12}$
Scores of 4 and 5 are both most likely.

5.6 Get ready

a $\frac{1}{2}$ **b** $\frac{2}{3}$
c $\frac{2}{3}$ **d** $\frac{1}{2}$

Exercise 5G

1 a Students' results
b i $\frac{1}{6}$ **ii** $\frac{3}{6} = \frac{1}{2}$ **iii** $\frac{2}{6} = \frac{1}{3}$
c Students' conclusions
2 a $\frac{1}{2}$
b, c Students' results and conclusions
3 a Students' results
b Throw the drawing pin more times.
4 Students' results
5 a Students' results
b Yes, because different languages use letters differently, affecting how often each letter appears.

5.7 Get ready

a 3 **b** 5 **c** 10

Exercise 5H

1

	Butterflies	Moths	Total
May	9	4	13
June	9	3	12
Total	18	7	25

2 a

	Walk	Bus	Cycle	Total
Boys	4	5	3	12
Girls	7	4	2	13
Total	11	9	5	25

b i $\frac{13}{25}$ **ii** $\frac{7}{25}$ **iii** $\frac{3}{25}$ **iv** $\frac{9}{25}$

3 a

	Cinema	Club	Bowling	Total
Boys	5	6	12	23
Girls	9	9	4	22
Total	14	15	16	45

b i $\frac{23}{45}$ **ii** $\frac{14}{45}$ **iii** $\frac{4}{45}$

4 a

	Orange	Lemonade	Milk	Total
Sandwiches	5	7	1	13
Biscuits	4	4	5	13
Crisps	8	7	1	16
Total	17	18	7	42

b i $\frac{18}{42} = \frac{3}{7}$ ii $\frac{16}{42} = \frac{8}{21}$ iii $\frac{4}{42} = \frac{2}{21}$ iv $\frac{4}{42} = \frac{2}{21}$

c John is right.

P(milk and biscuits) $= \frac{5}{42}$

P(orange and sandwiches) $= \frac{5}{42}$

5.8 Get ready

25 times

Exercise 5I

1 50 times

2 30 times

3 a 15 times

   b 45 times

   c 30 times

4 a 16 games

   b 14 games

5 a $\frac{3}{8} \times 60 = 22.5$; 22 or 23 red balls

   b $\frac{5}{8} \times 60 = 37.5$; 37 or 38 blue balls

6 95 claims

7 Students' numbers on star

   (average of numbers on star $= x - 5$)

   For example, if it costs 15p to play the game, $x = 15$.

   Average win should be $x - 5 = 10$p.

   Therefore numbers add up to $10 \times 6 = 60$

5.9 Get ready

1 $\frac{1}{4}$

2 $\frac{2}{5}$

Exercise 5J

1 $7:6:11$

2 $6:5:9$

3 14 supervisors

4 2 litres

5 £17.85

6 £50, £70

7 440 g butter, 200 g sugar, 700 g flour

8 a $\frac{1}{5}$ **b** $\frac{3}{10}$

Review exercise

1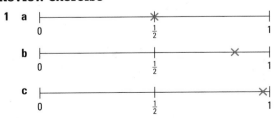

2 $\frac{2}{8} = \frac{1}{4}$

3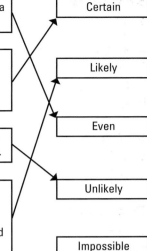

4 (fish, apple)   (fish, banana)

(fish, pear)   (lamb, apple)

(lamb, banana)   (lamb, pear)

(salad, apple)   (salad, banana)

(salad, pear)

5 a

	Black	White	Total
3-sided shape	1	4	5
4-sided shape	2	2	4
5-sided shape	2	0	2
Total	5	6	11

   b $\frac{4}{11}$

6 a (1, H), (2, H), (3, H), (4, H), (5, H), (1, T), (2, T), (3, T), (4, T), (5, T)

   b $\frac{1}{10}$

7 a

	London	York	Total
Boys	23	14	37
Girls	19	24	43
Total	42	38	80

   b $\frac{42}{80} = \frac{21}{40}$

8 a |———————×———|———————————|

    0   B $\frac{1}{2}$ 1

   b (green, heads), (green, tails), (blue, heads), (blue, tails), (yellow, heads), (yellow, tails)

9 $\frac{5}{12}$

10 $\frac{3}{8}$

11 a $\frac{7}{20}$ **b** $\frac{9}{20}$ **c** 0

12 a 0.2   **b** 15 counters

13 $x = 0.35$

14 0.4

15 a 0.25   **b** 35 times

16 $\frac{8}{40}$

17 £3622.50

Answers

18 Dunstan Building Society:
$\frac{4}{100} \times 2000 \times £80$
$2000 + 80 = £2080$ after one year
Chestman Building Society:
$12 \times 3.5 = £42$
$2000 + 42 = £2042$
$\frac{1}{100} \times 2042 = £20.42$
$2042 + 20.42 = £2062.42$
Therefore Dunstan Building Society gives the best return.

19 a 29 full portions   **b** £5.04

20 Robbie

21 The yellow horse has a 50% chance of moving.

22 Horse 1 cannot win as a score of 1 is not possible.
Horse 7 is most likely to win.

23 Students' own experiments.

Interpreting and displaying data

1

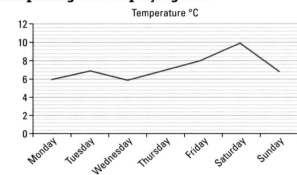

Temperature °C

2

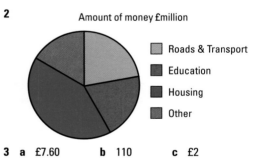

Amount of money £million

- Roads & Transport
- Education
- Housing
- Other

3 a £7.60   **b** 110   **c** £2
d When a scatter graph is drawn there is a positive correlation between the number of pages and the price of the book. A line of best fit can be drawn and estimates made.

4 Miss Khan

Average and range

1 Hatton: mean = 36.5; range = 8
Georgie: mean = 37.5; range = 24
Hatton's team were more consistent with a lower range but due to two high-scoring members the mean for Georgie's team was higher.

2 Any 3 with mean, mode or median of £8.97
e.g. £8.96   £8.97   £8.98

3 a 1, 2, 3, 4, 5; 1, 1, 4, 4, 5
b 1, 2, 3, 4, 5; 2, 2, 2, 4, 5
c 1, 2, 3, 4, 5; 1, 1, 1, 5, 7

4 50 minutes

5 Farmer Pearce: mean = 1477.5 g; range = 1000 g
Farmer Hicken has the larger mean but also the larger range so his lambs are less consistent. Some may be very large and others very small.

6

	Florida	Varadero	Red Sea
Average Max Temp °C	27	26.8	26
Average Min Temp °C	15	19.8	16
% probability rain	7.2	14	0

Florida has the highest temperature but it also has the greatest range of temperature.

Varadero's maximum temperature is only slightly lower but the temperatures are consistently high and don't drop at night. It has the most rain of the three resorts.

The best choice for most people is the Red Sea. The temperatures are less extreme, the maximum temperature is only 1° lower than Florida and there is no rain.

Probability

1 The probability of travelling to school by bus is $\frac{7}{30}$.

2 a He is only correct if each question has only two answers and he chooses at random.
b Most tests have four or five answers so he is unlikely to be correct.

3 $\frac{1}{2}$. At least two out of the three coins must be the same. So it is the probability that the other one matches these which is $\frac{1}{2}$.

4 $\frac{1}{9}$

5 0.3

6 $\frac{23}{100}$ or 23% or 0.23

Holiday	July	Aug	Sept	Total
Hotel	18	23	16	57
Self Catering	14	19	10	43
Total	32	42	26	100

Healthy living

1 Samantha ate 34.2 g of fat and 3 g of salt. Daisy ate 44.4 g of fat and 3.5 g of salt. Darren ate 40.8 g of fat and 2.9 g of salt. Samantha ate the least fat. Daisy ate the most fat and salt. Darren ate the least salt.

2 There are roughly 123 000 obese children in Year 6 and 57 000 obese children in Reception.

There are roughly 91 000 overweight children in Year 6 and 78 000 overweight children in Reception.

There are more obese children than overweight children in Year 6. There are more overweight children than obese children in Reception. There are more obese and overweight children in Year 6 than in Reception.

3 She should spend 12 minutes (0.2 hours) on flexibility, 24 minutes (0.4 hours) on aerobic exercise and 84 minutes (1.4 hours) on anaerobic exercise.

Learning to drive

1

Speed (mph)	Thinking distance (m)	Breaking distance (m)	Total distance (m)
20	6	6	12
30	9	14	23
40	12	24	36
50	15	38	53
60	18	55	73
70	21	75	96

2 Minimum cost = £757.49

3 £1920

Index